When a Parent is Sick

Helping Parents
Explain
Serious Illness
to
Children

Joan Hamilton, RN, BN, MSc(A)

Pottersfield Press, Lawrencetown Beach, Nova Scotia, Canada

The author gratefully acknowledges the support of the Queen Elizabeth II Health Sciences Centre, Halifax, Nova Scotia, Canada. Thanks to Gwen North for the design and layout of the previous editions.

The 1999 edition is available in French by contacting msgjeh@qe2.hsc.ns.ca

Front cover photograph by Fred Burge.

Canadian Cataloguing in Publication Data

Hamilton, Joan, 1958–
   When a parent is sick: helping parents explain serious illness to children

ISBN 1-895900-40-9

1. Parent and child.   2. Critically ill – Family relationships.
3. Parents – Death – Psychological aspects.   4. Children and death.
I. Title.

R726.5.H36 2001   362.1   C2001-900027-8
                         HAM

Pottersfield Press gratefully acknowledges the ongoing support of the Nova Scotia Department of Tourism and Culture, Cultural Affairs Division, as well as The Canada Council for the Arts. We acknowledge the financial support of the Government of Canada through the Book Publishing Industry Development Program for our publishing activities.

Printed in Canada

Pottersfield Press
83 Leslie Road
East Lawrencetown
Nova Scotia, Canada, B2Z 1P8
Website: www.pottersfieldpress.com

To order telephone toll-free 1-800-NIMBUS9 (1-800-646-2879)

THE CANADA COUNCIL | LE CONSEIL DES ARTS
FOR THE ARTS | DU CANADA
SINCE 1957 | DEPUIS 1957

NOVA SCOTIA
Tourism and Culture

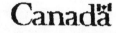

Canadä

Contents

Introduction

This book provides parents, grandparents, other family members, babysitters, and friends with some ideas and examples of how to talk to and respond to children throughout a parent's serious illness. Some of the ideas and examples have come from experts who have written books (see the selected titles in chapters 8 and 12). Other explanations and suggestions are my interpretations of what I have learned from these experts and as a registered nurse caring for cancer patients and their families. The examples in this book describe a parent who has cancer but certainly the principles or ideas apply to any type of serious illness. A mother is used in the examples to describe the parent who is sick.

At a time when so much is happening in a family's life, you may not have the time, energy and concentration to find the words to explain a diagnosis of a serious illness to your children. If you don't have the time now to read this entire book, the Quick Overview (pages 8-16) will give you the main points to consider as you talk to your children.

How children respond or react to what is happening in their lives varies a great deal. If a parent has concerns or feels that a child is having problems, that a child is struggling with things in a way that just doesn't seem right — seek out help. If there is a children's hospital in your area, see if it has a Child and Adolescent Mental Health program. Professionals there should be able to direct you to someone. Others who may be able to assist you include someone like a school counsellor, a family doctor, a health care professional (e.g. social worker, psychologist, nurse) who is caring for the sick parent, or someone from the Cancer Society or similar organizations.

The information in this book can help families faced with serious illness in two important ways — for some it will confirm or validate that they are on the right track with how they are handling things with their children, and for others it will help guide them through unknown territory.

Joan Hamilton
March 2001

Quick overview

What should you do?

- Tell your children what is happening as soon as possible. They will sense that something is wrong. It is far better for them to hear it from you than find out another way.

- Tell all your children at the same time, even if there is an age gap. The younger ones may not understand at the level of the older ones, but they will feel included. When the children know there are no secrets, they will be better able to support each other.

- Be open and honest. Children need your trust more than ever right now. Don't risk losing it.

- Children tend to cope best when they are well informed and there are no surprises about what is happening. Keep children up to date.

- You may want to practice or write down what and how to say things. This may not be your usual way to talk with your children, but explain that what you have to say is really important and you want to make sure you explain it correctly.

- Let other people caring for the children know how you have explained things and give them some direction on how to respond to children's questions, fears and behaviours. Some parents write down explanations or answers to questions so that others will know how to respond to the children.

- Sometimes, different generations have different ideas of how or when to include children when something like this happens. Some believe you shouldn't tell or involve children because you don't want to upset them. Some believe children should be protected from the pain. Experts now believe we should not protect children from what is happening in their own family and that children will have a smoother adjustment to change if they feel included and if they know, to their level of understanding, what is going on. Children then have the opportunity to work at, and to work through, their feelings at the same time as everyone else. It is important for parents to take the lead and instruct others on how to respond and what to say to the children.

- A check to gauge that you are open and honest with children is if you can talk freely with other adults on the phone or face to face, and not have to be too careful about what you are saying because the kids are around. Although they may not understand all of what you are saying, they have heard the words (e.g. chemotherapy and radiotherapy) in previous explanations to them. What they are hearing is not new, just being described a bit differently.

What should you talk about?

The disease

Tell children as soon as you can that their parent is sick.

Use the word "cancer." Soon, and sooner than you would believe, your children will hear the word cancer connected with the illness. Let them hear it from you first.

Name the specific cancer (use the words they will hear) and then explain, in words they will understand, what it means.

> "I am very sick."
> "I may look (seem) okay, but I am very sick."

> "I have a sickness (disease) called cancer."
> "There are many different types of cancer."

> "I have a type of cancer called leukemia. Leukemia means that there is cancer in my blood." ("I have cancer in one of my breasts.") ("I have cancer that started in my _____ and has spread to _____. ")

The plans over the next while (what is going to happen)

Explain the treatment(s) planned for the near future — or as much as you know. Will the parent be in hospital/at home? Will their appearance change? What will be the likely side effects of the disease or treatment?

Explain how things will change for the children, and who will be looking after them. Will they be staying in their own home?

Will they still be going to their usual activities? If plans are still uncertain/unknown, tell them you will let them know as soon as you know. Try to give your children even a rough idea of the length of time the treatment and recovery may take: months; by the season ("maybe after the end of the summer"); by a certain holiday or celebration; or, "We just don't know how long Mommy is going to be sick." "I am going to be sick for a long time before I can get better."

Information from other sources

It is amazing what children can hear in the neighbourhood, at school, or at a friend's house. Explain how information can get mixed up and what they should do if they hear something that conflicts with what you've told them.

> "If you hear something different from someone else, come ask me about it."
> "Daddy and I know best what is happening. If you hear something from someone else, come and talk to us."

Ongoing communication

Tell the children that you will keep them up to date and that if anything changes, you will let them know. Encourage them to ask questions and talk about what they are feeling.

> "Do you have any questions?"
> "Do you feel you understand what is happening?"
> "We want to make sure that you understand what is going on, so could you tell me in your own words what you think is happening?"
> "What are the kinds of things you are worried about?"
> "Do you feel like talking about anything?"

Addressing the future

- Tell your children that you will keep them up to date about the illness, treatment and planned hospital stays. Talk to them about any change of plans that may happen to their usual activities over the next few weeks or months and who will be taking care of them.

- For many parents, the hardest thing about explaining serious illness to their children is talking about the dying issue. Because of Terry Fox Day at school and/or because of the experiences of family, friends, and famous people, many school age children link cancer with dying. For most children, the question "Are you going to die?" quickly forms in their minds. As uncomfortable as it may be, this issue needs to be addressed in one of your early conversations. If you don't address it, children will think it is off limits to discuss, and it becomes a barrier to completely open communication. Important pieces of what children need to know to help them understand the whole picture are left out, and they are left with unanswered questions.

- You can bring it up in an indirect way: "Right now the doctors feel I am going to do fine and that I will get better, but if anything changes I will let you know." You can explain it in a direct way: "We don't know right now how I am going to do. If it looks like I am getting sicker, and that I might die, I will tell you." Or you can have an answer ready for when your child asks. Make sure you keep your promise if you tell them you will keep them informed.

- Your children may think about but never come right out and ask you, "Are you going to die?" They may want to protect you, or they may want to protect themselves. As painful as it may be, it is a piece of information they need.

• If you believe that your child will not link cancer with anything serious, remember that they will hear things from others who don't necessarily have the whole or the correct story.

Examples of ways to address the future (depending on your situation)

"Right now the doctors expect that I will be fine. With the type of cancer I have, the medicine usually kills all of the cancer."

"Right now everyone expects that I will do fine, and that the medicine will kill all the cancer. If things change and it looks like the cancer isn't going away, we will tell you."

"Some people do die from certain kinds of cancer, but with the type of cancer I have, we are all expecting that I will do just fine."

"Nobody is sure right now if they can make the cancer go away. We all need to hope (pray) very much that what they are trying to do will work."

"We will tell you if it looks like Mommy isn't going to get better'"

"The doctors don't think that I am going to get better. I am going to get some treatment that will hopefully slow the cancer down so that I can live for a few months longer."

"When it looks like Mommy is not going to live much longer, we will tell you."

How should you respond?

- When you tell your children, get a reading from them as to how much to tell them at a time. A child may only be able to hear so much, and then need to move on to something that is normal and familiar to them. If they return to play immediately after you have talked to them, they are returning to an activity they know, and to feelings that provide security in their world. Quickly changing the subject is normal.

- Children are normally self-centered — a crisis doesn't usually change this.

- The disruption that the illness causes in the child's life can be just as upsetting and be just as much of a blow as the illness itself. Children think the world revolves around them most of the time. This thinking does not usually change when there are difficulties in the family. Don't expect complete understanding. Try to be patient and not make children feel guilty for wanting to go on with their normal routine.

- Experts believe that children cope best when there are no surprises with what is happening. Keep children up to date.

- Don't try to predict how your child is going to deal with this. With a child, as with an adult, distress comes out in many different forms: anger, crying, pretending everything is alright, acting out, temper tantrums, regression (wetting the bed, no longer toilet trained, needing a bottle), intense physical activity, needing to be physically close to the sick parent, etc. Children don't have the advantage of always being able to talk about what and how they are feeling. They show their feelings in ways that they know.

• Distress may come out in childish ways — because they are children. Be patient and don't expect them to act more maturely than they behaved before the parent's illness.

• Don't expect a child to cope in a certain way. Don't force them to face an issue when they have given you a strong message that they are not ready to address it.

• Give children the opportunity to explore feelings, fears, and ideas so that you have a better understanding of how they are viewing things. "Have you been thinking about something that is going on that you want to talk to me about?" "Sometimes I feel scared (sad) about all this and wish that everything was the same as before. Do you ever feel this way?"

• Showing your feelings is usually more powerful than words. You can tell your children it's alright to cry or be sad, but it probably isn't as effective as showing them. Express your feelings but don't completely unload in front of your kids. They always need to feel that you are in control and that you can look after them. If you need to let loose with your emotions, get someone else to look after the kids while you have some time to let your guard down.

• Although a child may need a bit of slack now and then, for the most part, try to maintain their usual routine, rules and boundaries. Children are not ready to deal with choices at this time. More than ever they now need the security, stability and structure of knowing that some things haven't changed. Try to be consistent with normal rules.

Key points to consider

- As soon as you can, be open and honest with your children.

- Cover the dying issue right from the start. Probably the hardest thing for everyone will then be in the open and no one will have to be on their guard.

- Involve your children in what is happening so they feel included.

- Keep children informed about plans over the next while for them, their sick parent and their healthy parent.

- Avoid surprises whenever possible. Tell your children you will keep them up to date with what is going on with their parent. "If anything changes, we will let you know." If you tell them this, be sure and keep your promise.

- Tell them that if they hear things that are different from what you have told them, to come and ask you. You know best what is happening.

1. Things to consider as you talk to your children

Explaining serious illness to a child is one of the hardest things a parent could ever do. No one ever really feels completely prepared, comfortable or good at it. Most feel awkward and inadequate.

Talk to your children about what is happening as soon as possible. Children of all ages seem to have a built-in "something is wrong" detector. Although they may not realize what is wrong, they very quickly pick up that something is not right. If children are not soon told by a parent, another family member or a close family friend, they will hear about a parent's illness from someone else, often with wrong or incomplete information. Or they may interpret family disruption in their own way, blaming themselves and letting their imagination work overtime.

Not telling the truth, or not giving them all the information (at their level of understanding), can make things worse. If you are usually open and honest with your children, they need to hear what is going on from you first or you risk breaking the trust you have established with them over the years. Tell your children as soon as you are able — they are part of the family and part of this experience.

Children tend to cope best when they are well-informed and there are no surprises with what is happening. Keep children up to date. Being open and honest with them (on their level) ensures that they will continue to come to you if they have questions or hear something different from somebody else.

Children's friends, parents of friends, neighbours, teachers — everyone has their own version of what is taking place and what is going to happen. It is important to reinforce with your child that if they hear things from others that differ from what they have been told, they should discuss it with you. When a child learns that you are open and honest, he/she will soon realize that others outside the immediate family do not necessarily have reliable up-to-date information.

If possible, both parents should talk to the child. If the sick parent is able, decide together what to explain and how. If the sick parent is unable and the healthy parent just can't bring him/herself to do it, be selective in who does talk to the children. One or both parents should be present so that everyone knows what has been said.

When discussing things with your children, talk to all of them at the same time, even if there is an age gap. The younger ones may not understand at the level of the older ones, but they will feel a part of what is going on. You don't want "secrets" in the family. The children may be more likely to look to each other for support if they all know that nothing is being kept from anyone.

The way in which a parent explains the illness, its significance, treatment and changes in family life, will depend on the child's maturity level, past experience with sickness, and developmental stage. If you have children at different levels of understanding, you may have to explain the same thing in different ways so that each one has an explanation at their own level. The younger ones will pick up bits and pieces of the explanations you give to the older children. They will hear words that you will use in adult conversations and know that things have been discussed with them, even if they don't really understand what they are.

Explanations to your child should be in simple terms, at their level of understanding, but don't oversimplify by making light of the situation. All of a child's questions should be answered. If you are unsure why they are asking a question, try to find out where they are coming from with it. This may provide you with an opportunity to clear up misconceptions. If you can't answer a question, assure the child you will find out and get back with an answer. Clarify with a child that they understand the words you are using. To determine what a child understands, ask them to explain it back to you.

How you talk about things to your children is probably just as important as what you tell them. Lead into things gently. Don't overload them with information. Give them time to let things sink in. Keep answers short and to the point, and keep explanations simple. Be physically close to give them love and security. Children may not understand all the words, and what things mean for the present or future, but an open, honest and caring approach can help them feel secure and a part of what is happening. They can handle the news, and they will deal with it in their own way.

You may want to practice or write down what is to be said. This may not be the usual way you talk with your children, but you may feel more comfortable knowing what words you want to use. Anticipate questions and prepare answers. Having said that, try to be spontaneous in your discussion. Once you know how you want to explain certain things, try to let the conversation go its own way. If a child does ask a question and you are not prepared, answer it as best you can. Your child is looking for honesty, not a well-formed response.

Often, different generations have different ideas of how or when to include children when something like this happens. Some believe you shouldn't tell or involve children because you don't want to upset them. Some think children should be protected from the pain. Nowadays, experts say we should not protect children from what is happening in their own family. They believe that children will have a smoother adjustment to change if they feel they are included — if they know, to their level of understanding, what is going on. Children then have the opportunity to work at, and to work through, their feelings at the same time as everyone else. It is important that parents take the lead and instruct others on how to respond, and what to say to children about the situation.

Because it is important for children to hear the same explanations from all significant people in their lives (e.g. grandparents, babysitters, family, friends, and teachers), these adults should be kept informed of what and how things have been discussed. You may want to give these adults some direction on how to respond to children's questions, fears and behaviours. Make sure everyone who is explaining or reinforcing what is going on is saying the same thing. Some parents write down explanations to give to other significant adults in the child's life, so that they have a guide and can be consistent with the parents.

Don't present children with a lot of uncertainties in your explanations of what is happening. They need a sense of security.

A check to gauge that you are open and honest with your children is if you can talk freely with other adults on the phone or in person, and not have to be too careful about what you say because the children are within earshot. Although they may not understand all of what you are saying, they have heard the words before (e.g. chemotherapy and radiotherapy) in your explanation to them. What they are hearing is not new — just being described a bit differently.

Don't whisper. It implies secrets.

Sometime, somewhere (and usually sooner than you expect), children will hear from somebody that their parent is going to die "because they have cancer." Children do not necessarily realize that the information they hear from others can often be second, third and fourth hand, and therefore not reliable. If the "dying concern" has not been addressed at home and they hear about it elsewhere, it can obviously be very scary. Children may not want to explore what they have heard with you because they are scared, and because they want to protect you, just like you want to protect them. It is important that the "dying concern" be discussed, at some level, so that children feel fully informed and they recognize fiction from fact (see "Addressing the Future" in the Quick Overview on page 12).

Dealing with the disruptions the illness causes within family life is as hard for many children as dealing with the concerns of having a parent who is sick. Children are children. They think that the world revolves around them most of the time. This thinking does not usually change when there are difficulties in the family. Don't expect complete understanding. Try to be patient and not make children feel guilty for wanting to go on with their normal routine.

Dealing with feelings is hard work for children, just as it is for adults. Most experts believe that the more children express and explore a full range of feelings, the better able they are to cope with the present and the future. Children who receive a lot of emotional support seem to be able to adjust more easily.

Probably the most effective way to get children to talk about their feelings is for a parent to express their own (e.g. talk about fears, show sadness, cry, be angry). Although a parent may tell a child to let their feelings out, actually communicating your own feelings can demonstrate to a child that it is okay to do. If an adult never expresses feelings, the child may begin to wonder if things are as serious as people are saying, because no one seems upset. Having said all that, remember a person's coping doesn't suddenly change when a crisis occurs. If a child has been private with feelings and thoughts in the past, chances are she isn't going to suddenly open up and pour out her thoughts. Give her the opportunity to share her feelings, but don't force it.

Communicate your feelings as well as the information, (e.g. Daddy is sad because Mommy is sick. I miss her).

It takes time for children to learn what the illness means to them. As they learn, they will develop ideas and feelings, many of which may be new to them. These ideas and feelings need to be acknowledged and respected by parents and other adults. Letting children know that most of these feelings are experienced by other children in similar situations — that the feelings are normal — can be very reassuring.

Throughout an illness, information and feelings change. Children should be kept up to date without surprises. Parents should explore children's ideas on a regular basis, to ensure that facts are correct and expectations are realistic.

Children deal with serious illness in bits and pieces, at their own pace. Returning to their world of play and activities helps them regroup, feel secure, and act like nothing is wrong. When they feel ready again, they can face hearing more and maybe let themselves feel the feelings that go along with it. Normal routine and play should be encouraged as much as possible.

Children, at this time more than ever, need the security of knowing that their normal limits haven't changed when so many other things have. Try to keep a balance between normal routine and bending the rules when life is disrupted.

In your discussions with your children, never make promises you can't keep.

Ask children regularly, though not too often, if they have anything they would like to talk about, or if anything is bothering them.

Ongoing checks to ask yourself

- Does your child have a correct understanding of what is happening? Is your child up to date with information? Does your child feel included?

- Does your child have a general understanding of what is going to be happening over the next while with the sick parent?

- Have you addressed the future with your child?

- Do your children know how their day will change while their parent is sick?

- Have you left the channels of communication open?

- Do you regularly ask your children how they are doing, if they have any concerns they would like to talk about?

Examples of ongoing checks to ask your child

- I've told you a lot of things today. Do you have any worries or questions about what I've said?

- I want to make sure I've explained things to you in the right way. Can you explain it back to me?

- Sometimes you hear things about (cancer, leukemia). They may or may not have to do with your mother. Instead of keeping them inside, it is important that you ask me about them.

- What's on your mind?

2. Examples of what to say

The explanations have not been grouped according to age level as each child is different and each parent talks to their children differently. You might use bits and pieces of different explanations to arrive at your own way of explaining something.

Explaining ... Serious illness

I want to explain what's wrong with your mother and what's going to happen, so you will know what is going on.

You know your mother has not been feeling too well for a while now. Well, we found out today what is wrong.

Mommy is sick. It's not like a cold or measles or like feeling bad for a few days — she is very sick. She will be sick for a long time.

Mommy will have to stay in the hospital for a long time to get better. She doesn't want to be there but she is so sick she can't be home.

Mommy is very sick. It doesn't hurt, but the kind of sick she has means that she probably won't feel like herself for a long time.

The doctors aren't exactly sure what is going on with Mommy. She is sick, probably very sick, but the doctors aren't sure what is wrong.

There is something in Mommy's body that isn't supposed to be there. It can make Mommy very sick. It's not like when you fall or hurt your knee, or when you get a cold. It's something that makes your body get hurt on the inside.

Your mother is very sick but the doctors are almost sure they can make her better.

What I have told you is what I know and understand about what is wrong with your mother right now.

I will tell you if things change.

Right now Mommy is so sick she doesn't really care what's happening to her. When she feels better, she'll stop feeling that way.

I have to take the medicine for a long time. When the summer comes, I hope that things will be back to normal.

The cancer is different in everybody's body and we don't know what will happen. Sometimes the medication works very well to get rid of the cancer, sometimes it doesn't. Everyone is doing the best they can to make me better.

It may be a long time before I can do things with you that I usually do. Although my hair will grow back and I will look the same, I will probably still feel tired for a long time.

The doctors say I have an excellent chance of getting better.

If you have any questions at all, please ask me. I don't want you to worry about this all by yourself. We need to talk about things and be open with each other.

Explaining ... Disease and treatment

Disease — Cancer

I'm sick. I have a sickness called cancer. I am going to have to stay in the hospital so the doctors can give me some medicine (treatment/care) to help me get well. It takes a long time to get well when you have this kind of sickness.

There is something inside my body called cancer. The doctors are giving me medicine (treatment) so that it will go away.

There are many types of cancers. They are all different. Some cancers are cured quickly and easily by treatment, others are not. Sometimes you die because you have cancer, sometimes you don't.

Uncle Joe had a very different kind of cancer than I have. With the kind of cancer he had, people don't usually get better. I have a different kind of cancer than Uncle Joe had.

There are many types of cancers, more than 100. Some cancers grow very slowly, others grow fast. Some cancers can be cured, some can be greatly slowed down and with some, people do die after awhile because treatment does not work. There may be a period of time that the doctors don't know if treatment is going to work, and everyone has to wait and see.

Leukemia is a type of cancer.

Cancer is the name of a whole group of different diseases. Some are more serious than others. Some cancers make people die, some don't. Many cancers can be treated so that the person gets well again. In your mother's case . . .

Sometimes you hear scary things about cancer. There are different types of cancer. I'll tell you what I know about the kind of cancer your mother has.

Cancer treatment

Chemotherapy
Mommy is getting some medicine to help her get well. The medicine is called chemotherapy. It kills the cancer little by little.

Surgery
I have cancer in one of my breasts. I have to go to the hospital to have an operation. That means that the doctor will take my breast off.

Radiotherapy
You know the special camera that takes pictures of the inside of you (your bones) at the hospital. It's called an x-ray. There's also a special kind of machine like an x-ray machine that helps the cancer go away. It's like medicine, and it's called radiation. The radiation goes into the body and kills the cancer cells. Mommy will have some purple marks on her skin to show where to point the machine so that the radiation kills the cancer.

Treatment — General

The nurses and doctors are looking after Mommy and giving her things to get her better. She can't come home right now although she wishes she could.

The doctors think the medicine will work. We hope it will.

The doctors are giving me medicine to help me get well.

Mommy can't take the medicine by drinking or eating it, so she has a tube (like a long straw) that goes into her body and the medicine goes in that way.

Doctors know a lot about taking care of people when this happens.

Treatment is what makes you get better. It is also called therapy.

Chemotherapy is when the cancer is treated with very strong medicines (drugs) that kill the cancer.

The treatment sometimes makes people look and feel even sicker than they did before starting the treatment, but that's what has to happen so I can get better in the long run. I will feel better again after all the treatment has stopped.

Side effects are uncomfortable reactions — like feeling sick, your hair falling out or feeling really tired.

Your mom's mouth is very sore. It hurts when she talks so she won't be able to talk very much.

Explaining ... Why a parent is sick

Nobody really knows why I got sick. It just happened. I didn't want to get sick and nobody made me get sick.

It's not something you can get (catch) from me. I can't give my sickness to anyone.

Although you are in the same family you are your own person. You are different from me. You are very healthy and will probably live for a long time.

You had nothing to do with your mommy getting sick. Nothing you said, did or thought made your mommy sick.

We don't know why your mother got sick. Nobody can answer that. It's one of those questions that can't be answered.

One of the hardest things we have to learn and accept is that some questions do not have answers.

Mommy is not sick because you were bad.

I don't have all the answers. I don't understand some things.

Mommy isn't sick because God is mad at her. God wants everyone to be well and happy.

God didn't want Mommy to get sick. We don't know why this happened.

Explaining ... What may happen in the future

Your mom is very sick. Right now the doctors feel she is doing well and there is no reason to think she won't get better. If there comes a time when it looks like your mom isn't doing well, I will tell you. Right now, though, no one is thinking that.

Some people do die of cancer but a lot of people get better and live to be old.

We think the treatment will work. We hope it will work.

The doctor thinks I will be fine. Lots of people who get the kind of cancer I have live for a long time, as long as anyone else. We will tell you if anything changes.

Right now, the doctors say that Mommy is doing fine, the medicine is working and is making her better. If things change, and the medicine stops working, or it looks like she may die, I will tell you.

Many people who have cancer live for a long time, as long as anyone else.

I may not live as long as other people. Nobody can say right now.

I am probably only going to live for a few more months. Nobody knows exactly when I will stop living. When it looks like I am not going to live much longer, we will tell you.

If anything changes, we will tell you.

Right now everyone expects that I will do fine, and that the medicine will kill all the cancer. If things change and it looks like the cancer isn't going away, we will tell you.

Nobody is sure right now if they can make the cancer go away. We all need to hope (pray) very much that what they are trying to do will work.

We'll tell you if it looks like Mommy isn't going to get better.

Most people get better when they have the sickness that your mother has. Sometimes, though, someone does get more and more sick until they can no longer live, and they die. We hope very much that your mother is going to do just fine, and get all better.

Sometimes things happen to people that keep them from getting better.

I will tell you if things change.

Your mother may not live as long as most people do.

It's okay to worry that your mother may not get better — everybody does. Try not to worry about it all the time though. Your mother also wants you to carry on with your life.

Your mother is not getting better — she's getting sicker.

If Mommy gets really sick and we are worried about her dying, we will tell you.

Your mom is very sick. The medication (treatment) she is getting is working to try and make her better (kill all the cancer cells). The doctors feel that she will do very well and that she will get better. Every once in awhile the treatment doesn't do everything that it should, or other things happen and people don't get better — they die. We expect your mom will do just fine. I just wanted you to know that there is a small chance that the treatment won't work. We will let you know if anything changes.

Explaining ... Change in appearance and activity

It may be a long time before your mother is like she used to be. She is going to be tired for a long time.

The medicine is very strong. It helps me to get better but while it does that it makes me _____ .

I know I look different on the outside but on the inside I'm the same and I love you very much. Maybe you could put a picture of me by your bed so you remember how I usually look.

Sometimes the chemotherapy will make your mom tired, lose her appetite and make her lose weight.

Mommy's hair may fall out but it will grow back in after she finishes treatment.

I want to do the things that we used to do, but I just don't have the energy right now. Let's think of some things we could do with you sitting on the bed with me.

Explaining ... Having some normal times

Sometimes we have to pretend that everything is okay and not think about the cancer. It's okay to do that because we know what's really happening.

You can play and be with your friends and do what you usually do. Your mother doesn't want you to be sad and sit around all day.

There will be times that you will forget what is happening with your mother and you'll just act normally. That's fine. We can't think about this all the time.

Explaining ... Telling their friends

Some friends and kids at school may act differently towards you. This is usually because they feel uncomfortable and they don't know what to do or say.

It may be good to tell _____ (close friend) what is happening to Mom so he knows what's going on. Then he'll understand why things are a bit different and why you may be acting a bit differently.

Your mom being sick is not a secret, but you may not want to tell everyone. If you tell your close friends, then they will know why things may be a little different around here.

Sometimes kids make fun of things they don't understand or they say things because they feel uneasy. Although it takes a lot of nerve, if you explain things to them one at a time, in a quiet way, it would help them understand and they would probably stop being weird around you.

Sometimes friends are afraid they will upset you if they ask questions or talk to you about your mom. It's important to let them know what you are comfortable (or not comfortable) talking about.

Explaining ... Visiting the sick parent

Sometimes she will feel so sick and tired that she won't be able to talk. When this happens, you can make a card or picture and send it to her because you won't be able to go visit her. Sometimes she'll feel okay. When she feels okay, you can go and visit.

When Mommy is feeling very tired and sick, I will be looking after her. She won't feel good enough to have you come and see her but as soon as she feels okay she will want you to come and see her.

Your mom will not be as strong to fight off colds and a lot of the things that kids get. When there is a big chance that she could get sick from other people, you won't be allowed to go into her room to see her. Your mom needs to save all her energy right now to get well. As soon as things are better, she wants you to visit.

Explaining ... Feelings

Even if you don't think it does, sometimes your mom being sick can affect all kinds of things. Some kids find it hard at school, some kids can't concentrate on anything. Some kids can't sleep, some kids can't help but behave badly. Usually this is because they are worried and because everything is mixed up — their feelings and their life. If you are feeling any of this, let's talk to see if we can work at making things better.

Different people feel different things about what is happening. Try to let your feelings out in some way, so they don't get all bottled up inside you.

You may feel things that you've never felt before.

Many children and adults feel very mixed up about all this. Sometimes it helps if you talk about it.

Maybe you would like to talk about it so we can try to understand what you're feeling.

This must feel like more hurt than you can stand.

When you tell me what is wrong, I can try and understand your feelings.

Sometimes you have to try things to find out what makes you feel better. I'll try and help you.

Sharing your problems and worries with people who care about you can sometimes help.

Worrying about things can take up a lot of energy. Talking about them usually helps.

Everybody shows their worries differently.

We can't make our feelings go away just because we want them to.

Everyone will find their own way of dealing with what is happening.

For many people, they feel better if they talk about what they are feeling. You may want to talk to me, but sometimes you may want to talk to someone else.

We are all going to have trouble dealing with this. We will probably feel many of the same things, so I may want to let some feelings out — or you may want to talk to me.

I am going to have bad days when I won't cope with things very well and you may have bad days too.

This will take time to get used to.

We are all going to have to prepare ourselves for some difficult times ahead.

I want you to ask me any questions you have. I may get upset when I answer them — not upset with you, but because I'm sad. It's important that we talk about them even if it hurts sometimes.

Sometimes you may not want to ask a question because you are afraid to hear the answer — don't think about it too much before asking.

The nurse told me that sometimes people in a family are afraid to show each other how scared or worried they are, so nobody ever lets each other know what they are feeling. If this happens, everybody keeps everything bottled up inside and you can feel very lonely and scared. I hope that we can show and talk about our feelings.

You may not feel that I'm spending enough time with you, or paying enough attention. If this happens, tell me — we can talk about it.

A lot of people think they should always be bright and cheery around your mom, and protect her from the sadness and things they are feeling. I think probably she would like to talk about some of these feelings, but doesn't want to upset you either. It's okay to tell her that you are sad or worried. You may find you are both feeling the same kind of things.

Sometimes you can't say or put into words what you are feeling. Don't worry, your mom knows how much you love her.

We all have our own way of showing Mom that we love her.

You don't need to act any differently around your mom. In fact, it would be strange if you changed how you are with her.

Your mom wants to hear about you and what's happening in your life. She doesn't want to always talk about being sick. Talk to her about normal things (your friends, school, activities).

I may seem very sad and upset, but I'm still able to take good care of you. I just need to let some sadness out sometimes. I'm still in control of our lives and can take care of you.

When something upsetting happens in a family, different people in your family can feel and act differently. Sometimes you can feel a certain way some of the time, and then you feel a different way another time. Then there are times when you forget that anything is wrong. Sometimes feelings get all mixed up and you can't tell how you are feeling.

Some people may feel mad, some sad, and some may not know quite what they are feeling. Some don't want to talk about things, others may want to talk about it a lot. The important thing is that everybody in the family needs to remember there is no right or wrong way to feel. We all have to be patient and understanding about how others are feeling and acting.

Explaining ... Feeling sad

I'm so sad Mommy is sick that you will probably see me crying now and then. When you are thinking about Mommy and feeling sad, you can cry too. Maybe sometimes we will cry together. Maybe it will make us feel better.

One of the ways people show how upset they are is by crying.

One of the ways people show how worried they are or how much they miss someone is by crying and being sad some of the time.

Mommy being sick makes me sad and scared. It's okay if you feel that way.

Crying helps let out sad feelings. Maybe you will feel better.

Sometimes crying helps us feel better.

I feel so sad that I have to cry. It's hard to see Mommy so sick, but holding and loving you helps . . . it makes me feel better.

Letting your feelings out can make you sad and make you start crying, but it is important to let these feelings out so they don't build up inside you.

Explaining ... Being worried

Many kids, when they find out a parent is very sick and going to be in the hospital for a long time, wonder about a lot of things. What have you been wondering about?

It's normal for you to think about these kinds of things. Let's talk about _____ .

I will be spending time looking after Mom in the hospital, but I will also be at home sometimes to be with you. When I'm not going to be home, _____ will come and stay with you.

You can't catch cancer. You can't get it from someone else.

You may worry that you have, or will get, cancer. Many kids do when a parent gets cancer. This is usually because of everything that is going on and because you are worried. If you are concerned, please talk to me.

Explaining ... Feeling angry

Sometimes kids feel mad when a parent gets sick. It changes a lot of things for a long time. It is normal to be mad at times.

Sometimes it helps to get some of that anger out. Some kids find it helpful to _____ .

Sometimes we may get mad at each other, but we all know that even though we do, we still always love each other.

It is normal to feel angry that this has happened. You can show your anger by _____ . You may not show your anger by _____ .

I feel angry sometimes — angry at a whole bunch of things. I'm angry that everything has changed and things seem all mixed up. I'm angry because I can't do fun things anymore, and I'm angry because I can't spend time with you like I want to. You may feel like this too . . . .

Explaining ... Feeling guilty

Sometimes kids think back to when they were bad or thought bad things about their mother and wish it had never happened. Your mother loves you very much, and she forgave you for those things a long time ago. She knows that you love her.

Don't feel bad if you aren't sad or thinking about your mother all the time. She wouldn't want that. She still wants you to carry on with your normal life — and play and be with your friends.

We can always think of things we could have done differently, but we can't go back and change things. We do the best we can at the time.

It's okay to laugh and play and take your mind off your worries for awhile.

I feel guilty sometimes because I feel mad that your mom's cancer has changed everything. Then I remind myself that I'm not mad at your mom, I'm mad at the cancer.

3. A child's understanding of and response to a parent's serious illness

Children under 2½ years

Developmental stage

- totally focused on self;
- concerned with being separated from parents;
- afraid of hospitals and procedures — for him/herself and others;
- understands "all gone" but doesn't necessarily see that something is final;
- lives in present, minimal understanding of the concept of time;
- can't understand explanations (little value in trying to explain);
- assumes all things come back or are the same as before.

Understanding of illness

- may understand "hurt," "boo-boo," "sad";

- can't differentiate between a parent being away for a short time or being away for a long time;

- can sense loss of, or change in, something, but can't verbalize it;

- unable to understand the impact of, or what it means to be, sick.

Reactions/How children cope

- can't verbalize the discomfort and insecurity felt at being separated from parent, but knows something is amiss.

Under 5 months

- often cries, shows distress.

5 months–2½ years

- may act out and protest, hoping that parent will return (if parent not in the home). When parent does not return, behaviour often changes to sadness, withdrawal, loss of interest in usual activities.

- may have changes in sleeping and eating.

- does not want to be separated from healthy parent. May cling and scream when parent tries to leave (more so than usual).

How a parent can help

- As much as possible, try to keep a normal routine.

- Try to keep your child in familiar surroundings.

- Give your child frequent and lengthy periods of love and attention, reassurance and hugging. He/she may be inconsolable at first.

- Explain changes in terms of how they will affect your child.

- Try not to expose your child to too many different people.

- Try and arrange a consistent, comforting person to spend a lot of time with your child as quickly as possible.

- Take toys to the hospital when visiting so your child has something to do.

Toddlers (about 2½–5 years)
Developmental stage

- parents are the main focus;

- thinks very simply and concretely;

- concerned primarily with being separated from consistent caregivers;

- understands today, yesterday (already happened), and the possibility of something happening later;

- does not understand the concept of "the future," it's too abstract;

- spends a lot of time at play — pretending, making up, fantasizing;

- believes world revolves around him/her;

- reacts to feelings, not facts.

Understanding of illness

- beginning to understand some parts of the body (tummy, heart), but has little understanding of body function;

- generally views "hurt" and "sick" as short term events. "Very" sick or "really" sick may not mean any more to them than "sick";

- views "sick" as changes in activity, changes in speed of movement, change in appearance, decreased communication;

- believes illness is caused by a specific action and getting better will just happen or will come about by doing what the doctor says;

- believes they caused the person to be sick.

Reactions/How children cope

- react to the changes they feel around them, not to the sickness (because they don't understand the meaning or impact);

- express the discomfort that they are feeling at being separated from parent through changes in behaviour, or by asking for parent. Usually too young to express feelings.

- often regress. Children often cannot communicate or express themselves in words, so they communicate the only way they know how — behaviourally (physically). Children may also regress because they are not getting the usual praise from the sick parent for accomplishing tasks.

- will get clues on how to act by watching others, e.g. if others are crying they will cry;

- may feel responsible for causing illness, as they believe they control it;

- may become very active — running, jumping, yelling. Keep moving to show themselves and others that they are not sick, (and to get attention they are being denied).

- may play as normal (this does not mean they are unaffected);

- may listen to your explanations of what is happening, then quickly return to play;

- sadness, concerns and fears are intermittent;

- may make up little games of going to hospital;

- may be angry at sick parent for abandoning them;

- may be angry at all family members for the changes and disruption the sickness is causing;

- may attach themselves very closely to a "substitute" parent;

- may repeatedly ask about where parent is, why she/he has not returned, what she/he is doing.

How a parent can help

- Try to give your children extra love and attention whenever you can. If that is not possible, try to find someone they trust who can spend some extra time with them.

- Hug your child, maintain physical closeness. Give concrete, simple answers to questions.

- Reassure your child that he/she will be taken care of.

- Explain and reinforce that they did not do anything to make the parent sick.

- Explain to the child that the parent is not sick because of something bad the parent did.

- Share your feelings in a simple way (I hurt inside, I'm sad, I miss Mommy).

- When providing the child with information, be matter-of-fact and brief. A child needs concrete answers. After the discussion, you may want to share your feelings. Children at this age do not usually understand how this will affect them, so they are not sure how to react.

- Reassure the child that he/she, or the well parent, are not sick — that they are fine.

- Don't assume they don't understand what is going on. They may have a reasonable idea about the seriousness of the situation. Explore what they know and understand.

- Try to keep your child in familiar surroundings (it creates less disruption).

- Use your normal voice when explaining what is happening (whispers imply secrets).

- Keep some of your child's games, toys and books at the hospital for his/her visits. Prepare the child for periods of being sad, angry, upset, and mixed up.

- Although you should not hide your emotions, when you are actually explaining something that is going on, you should try to maintain a degree of composure so that the child does not feel upset or uncomfortable with your behaviour. The child always needs to feel that you "have it together" enough that you can take care of him/her. Your child will probably not feel comfortable asking questions if you are so focused on your emotions that you are having trouble with your explanations or answers. Remember children haven't had the experience to understand how this will affect them. They aren't sure how to react. Don't expect them to react in any certain way.

- Encourage physical activity. It's usually helpful in releasing a number of feelings.

- Encourage expression of emotions through music, drawing, painting, etc.

- Try to be patient when children seem selfish about how the illness is affecting them — they don't know how to look at things any other way.

Young school age (about 5–8 years)

Developmental stage

- parents are main focus;
- still very much dependent on parents;
- concerned about their own safety and safety of family;
- focused on family life and routine;
- interested in bodily functions;
- learning to follow rules;
- place importance on being the same as their friends;
- continue to pretend a lot in play;
- do activities outside of the family;
- starting to think logically;
- has clear understanding about past, present and tomorrow, still has unclear idea of long term future;
- self-centered;
- want to complete tasks on own;
- aware of right and wrong.

Understanding of illness

- can usually understand the difference between a simple and serious illness;
- understand that treatment helps you get well;

- have usually heard of "cancer" at school (e.g. Terry Fox Day) and therefore often equate cancer with death, or cancer with older people;

- may not be able to differentiate parent's fate from their own (what happens to parent will happen to them);

- concerned about what will happen in next couple of days — not necessarily down the road;

- will express feelings about what is happening;

- may ask concrete questions — "How did Mommy get cancer?" "Will I get it?";

- want to understand biological processes of what is wrong — sometimes more so than being concerned with what it means for parent to be sick;

- may believe that parent got sick because the parent did something bad;

- defines illness as how it affects his/her life — normal routine, activities, what the sick parent and child were doing or planning to do together;

- have some understanding of sickness and illness being life threatening.

Reactions/How children cope

- concerned that they are different from peers (e.g. parent no longer picking child up from soccer practice, grandmother looking after household, not able to afford to continue with certain activities);

- concerned about friends' and schoolmates' reactions and how to respond to their questions;

- confused by the power and depth of their feelings;

- may try hard to appear the same as usual (with crying and other feelings expressed in private);

- may focus on hospital equipment, technical things;

- want to continue as normal with outside activities;

- angry if usual activities are disrupted (e.g. can't get to soccer practice);

- angry if parent promised to go or do something with them and now parent is sick;

- sometimes wish it was other parent who got sick;

- feel guilty for feeling angry, for being healthy, for wanting to have fun when parent is sick.

How a parent can help

- Give child a lot of opportunity to talk, but be prepared as well to just "be together."

- Present child with clear information as to what is happening with sick parent.

- Reassure child that he/she will continue to be cared for.

- Reassure child that family will stay together (if true) while parent is sick.

- Reassure child that it is normal to feel angry and/or to sometimes wish it was the other parent who was sick.

- Keep hospital visits and discussions brief unless child desires otherwise. Keep games, toys and books at hospital so child has something to do.

- Remember that children will quickly return to the security of play, pretend and distraction when they have heard enough.

- Try to be patient when children seem selfish about how the illness is affecting them — they don't know how to look at things any other way.

- Recognize that scrapes and bruises are still significant events in a child's life. Reassure the child that they are not life threatening and that they are different than the sick parent's situation.

- Prepare explanations of illness, treatment and equipment. Child may focus on this because bodily function is such a focus now in their normal development.

- Prepare child for what to expect when visiting parent in hospital.

- If you don't explain what is happening, children will make sense in their own way by using their imagination and incorrect information.

- Regularly explore the child's understanding of what is happening.

- Ask frequently if he/she has any questions.

- Show your feelings so your child is encouraged to share his/hers.

- Reinforce that the parent is not sick because the parent (or child) did or thought something bad.

- Encourage physical activity.

- If a child is having difficulty releasing sad feelings, consider drawing the feelings out through a sad movie, story or song. Don't force.

Older school age (about 8–12 years)

Developmental stage

- starting to move outside family to develop relationships;

- shifting focus from family to friends;

- ask "how?" questions, searching for understanding and answers, how things work;

- absorbing new knowledge as fast as possible;

- want to accomplish tasks at school, play, and in home (chores);

- aware of right and wrong;

- understand what is socially acceptable;

- know they are part of the future;

- beginning to think abstractly;

- think logically — thinking based on facts most of the time.

Understanding of illness

- the meaning of the illness is primarily centered around how it affects the child socially;

- illness equals what the child sees as symptoms (tired, no hair, limitations in activities);

- child does not necessarily understand reason for symptoms or disease process;

- familiar with what cancer is — knows that there are different kinds of cancer.

Reactions/How children cope

- tend to manage with normal activities better than younger children because they are somewhat less dependent on parents. However, emotionally the child is struggling to be grown up and wants to show this by being independent. May try to cover up showing feelings (e.g. crying) because they want to be grown up, and showing feelings like crying would be childish.

- may focus more on how parent's illness has disrupted their life rather than show concern for sick parent;

- happy about having more independence, but unhappy about having added responsibility;

- wants specific information about prognosis and treatment;

- may question physicians', nurses' and hospital's ability to care for parent;

- afraid they themselves may not be healthy;

- concerned with rituals and traditions;

- talks about feelings not only in terms of him/herself but also how others feel;

- shares grief, sadness with others;

- may blame themselves for illness;

- commonly will show anger before sadness;

- commonly hide feelings from peers, but take these feelings out on family members.

How a parent can help

- Encourage child to continue involvement with friends and outside activities.

- Give some added tasks, but don't overload your children. Focus on tasks that apply to them (e.g. make own lunch).

- Try not to get frustrated with their self-centered approach to life. Be patient when a child seems selfish about how the illness is affecting them — they don't know how to look at things any other way.

- Reassure children that they are healthy.

- Supply enough accurate information so that the child is able to think logically about what is happening.

- Share own concerns, feelings, fears. This may normalize or help them sort out their own feelings.

- Child's "bad" behaviours may be the way that upsetting feelings are coming out. Instead of punishing, try to talk.

- Because it is "not cool" for the child to show physical affection, you will usually need to be the one to initiate hugging and cuddling. Don't do it in front of others (especially child's friends), unless this was an okay thing to do before.

- Allow them to participate (if they wish) in the care of the sick parent with tasks that are appropriate (e.g. helping bring Mommy lunch, straighten blankets, rub arm).

- "Role play" situations to practice how the child can react to peers' comments and questions.

- Predict what the child may encounter and walk them through the emotions to reduce surprises.

- Offer to help talk to the child's friends and their parents. Many of these friends may have strong feelings too.

- Be patient and understanding when your child lashes out at you. She/he feels safe showing her/his feelings to you.

- Try to protect your child from assuming the role of the sick parent.

Adolescents

Developmental stage

- developing and expanding relationships outside the family;

- trying to be more independent of parents, withdrawing from family;

- very self-conscious of body changes;

- struggling to be the same as friends and wanting to "fit in," experiencing a lot of peer pressure;

- focused on relationship with friends, but still dependent on family in many ways;

- thinking about their future;

- self-centered;

- thinking logically/abstractly;

- disagreeing frequently with parents over rules, values;

- moody;

- experimenting;

- wanting to be self-reliant;

- friends replacing parents for advice, support, companionship;

- still needing roots, home, intimacy and love of parents.

Understanding of illness

- general understanding of how body works;

- familiar with "cancer," understands that there are different types and varying outcomes;

- understands significance of serious illness;

- illness equals what they see as symptoms (and they understand the reason for the symptoms);

- illness equals possible death and non-being.

Reactions/How a teen copes

- struggles to set out on own, yet stay close to sick parent;

- very close (physically and emotionally) at times, and then withdraws completely to be with friends;

- worries about parent's future;

- has understanding of how others are feeling;

- concerned with discomfort, pain and suffering of sick parent;

- afraid to feel too much, afraid to let feelings show;

- worried that opening up or releasing feelings would cause them to completely break down;

- usually cope better than younger children because parents aren't the only people in their lives;

- if friends show support through family crisis and disruption, teen is reassured that no matter what happens, friends will still care;

- may look for the meaning or value of parent being sick;

- anger may be directed toward any family member, or the sick parent.

How a parent can help

- Acknowledge how hard it must be to feel torn between spending time with parent and spending time with friends. Try not to judge this. The teen is struggling with social pressure that commonly preoccupies adolescents. It is important that they carry on with some of their normal activities with friends.

- Don't pile too much responsibility on your teen for house and family, or make them assume adult roles.

- Involve them in some decision-making and activities.

- Encourage them to be with friends. Friends often provide a valuable support group for them.

4. Keeping a bit of "normal" in your child's day

For most families, the journey with a sick parent is up and down. During times when a parent is doing okay, daily routines can run quite smoothly and children go on with their usual lives of school and friends. When a parent is sick, having treatment, or recovering, children can feel a change in their lives as daily routines and relationships are commonly disrupted.

It is important to think about keeping some part of family life as routine or as "normal" as possible. This is often difficult to do, especially if a parent is in hospital and the other parent is spending a lot of time with them. Try protecting part of the day so that what happens during this time can feel somewhat like "normal" family time.

When it is possible to do so, plan, for example, to protect bed-time (or wake up time, or supper time) as a time to create some "normal" for your children. Let them (and others) know that this is going to be family time and for that hour or more, it will just be a time for the family to be together. Put a note on the doorbell asking people to please not disturb you between certain hours, say 6-8 p.m., as this is family time. As well, leave a message on your answering machine telling people that you won't be answering the phone during these times and turn the ringer off. For both parents and children, it can be a relief knowing there won't be disruptions.

If possible, don't use these times to introduce new information or plans. If children bring up questions, concerns or feelings, this uninterrupted time is ideal to discuss things, but let them be the ones to start these conversations. Otherwise, do what you would normally do during this time — play, read, cuddle. Children (like parents) need breaks through this journey where they can feel that things are normal.

If grandparents, relatives, or friends are temporarily living in the house, looking after the children, give them this time off, explaining you and the children need a little bit of private time together.

Visiting in hospital

When children visit the hospital, don't expect them to behave differently than they would otherwise. It is not natural for most children to sit quietly at the bedside. Very quickly it feels unnatural and forced, especially when they may be feeling uncomfortable in the hospital environment. Bring toys, games and books so that children can play alongside their parent after they have said their greetings and gotten caught up on what has been going on. This creates a more normal kind of togetherness for both the sick parent and the children.

Encourage children to talk about what has been going on in their lives, the good and the bad.

If friends ask how they can help, suggest they get a new toy or game that can be left at the hospital in the parent's room.

If a parent is feeling up to it, bring in a movie and have a movie night. Many hospitals have portable VCRs. Children can lie down beside their parent and watch a movie, creating a bit of "normal" for everyone.

Talk to staff about having some private time.

If children can't or don't want to visit the hospital, give them an opportunity to stay in touch by phone, letters, cards, pictures, audiotaped messages or stories.

5. Children's reactions to a seriously ill parent

When a parent becomes sick, things usually change. With each change a child experiences some loss of how things were before the illness.

Just like adults, children react or cope with loss and disruption in a variety of ways. A child's reaction and way of coping usually includes a wide range of feelings, behaviour and reactions. The purpose of coping is to help a person manage with what is happening.

Like adults, children don't plan how they are going to cope — it just happens, depending on how they interpret everything that is going on. You shouldn't expect a child's coping to change a great deal with the news that a parent is very sick. If you have a child who keeps to him/herself and doesn't talk about feelings very much with you, chances are he/she isn't going to open up at this time. Or, if your child usually asks a lot of questions about everything, and needs to know exactly what is going on, there is no reason to think he/she will act differently now. Make sure your expectations of your children's coping — of how they are handling things — are realistic. You may want or expect to see something from them that just isn't going to happen.

Children respond with children's emotions, feelings and reactions. They respond in childish ways because they are children. Distress may come out in childish ways because they are children. Most kids are very self-centered in everything they think or do. Dealing with a parent's illness does not typically change that thinking or behaviour.

Some feelings and behaviours may not appear to be helpful in overall adjustment. Generally these feelings or behaviours are short-lived, and help a child get through a particular period of time. Children can't typically explain what or how they are feeling in words, so they express themselves in ways that they do know — through their behaviour. Some of the behaviours are ways of releasing anger or hurt or sadness. Some actions are to express frustration at the changes that are taking place around them. Children do not necessarily know the adult ways of working through sadness, reacting to disruptions or dealing with concerns. An adult may take a long walk with a friend and talk out their concerns. A child may disobey and challenge as a way of letting out their concerns.

Usually what children feel and how they deal with things change over time.

Coping with what is happening is hard work. It can take a long time, with a lot of changes in how children think, feel and behave, before they are able to carry on with daily activities with ease.

A child's reactions throughout a parent's illness may appear inappropriate or insensitive. Remember, a child does not usually have a lot of past experience to draw from, and therefore does not understand the impact the illness will have. As well, children generally move rapidly from one subject to another when they feel they have received an answer. When you sit and talk about the illness to your children, keep it short and to the point. After you have asked them if they have any questions or concerns or if they want to talk about anything, don't expect them to sit around and mull things over with you. They will deal with what they have heard in their own way and in their own time. Teens may immediately head out to be with friends; younger children may return to their world of play; little ones may want your physical love. They all head back to normal and familiar events in their lives. They have heard what you have said and will probably want to get on with something else. Children have scattered reactions, scattered episodes of sadness or anger. They put their feelings aside for periods of time, live normally, then come back to the feelings — just like adults.

As much as possible, try to keep a normal routine. There is stability and security in routine. It is very important that everyone in the family — the sick parent, the healthy parent and the children — continue to have as much "normal" in their lives as possible. The sick parent needs to have times when he or she pretends there is nothing wrong. Children, even more so, need to have periods of time when they pretend everything is fine. What this means is that children shouldn't be made to feel guilty for having fun, for laughing, for wanting to carry on with usual activities. Express to the child that it is okay to carry on as normal, that it is okay to laugh and have fun. Just as the sick parent is working hard to get well and the healthy parent will look after them, the children are to continue with school, to do their after school activities, and to play.

Over time, children learn what the sickness means. They experience change in daily life and they will think about what is happening. With these changes, they will experience new and uncomfortable feelings. Don't try to predict how your child is going to deal with a parent being sick and changes with home life. In a child, as with an adult, distress comes out in many different forms: anger, crying, pretending everything is alright, acting out, temper tantrums, regression (wetting the bed, no longer toilet trained, needing a bottle), intense physical activity, needing to be physically close to the sick parent, etc. Children don't necessarily have the advantage of being able to talk about what and how they are feeling. They show their feelings in ways they know. They may not want to show their feelings in front of you.

Children may find another adult to talk to about what is happening. Talking to someone they are not as close to is somehow safer, less uncomfortable. If this happens, keep that adult up to date with information and the kinds of things you want your child to understand.

It is very important to respect a child's coping. You shouldn't try to push your child to react in a certain way. *You* may want to have a heart-to-heart with your teen. *You* may think that your child should have a good cry and let everything out, but that may not be what your child needs. What you can do is provide them with the opportunity to talk about how they are feeling or express how you are feeling by doing it yourself, but don't try to force things out of them.

When a child's behaviour doesn't change

Children may act like nothing has happened because:

- they can't face the reality of what they have been told or what is happening;

- they need to act like everything is okay (go out to play, go to meet friends);

- they want the security of something that is normal to counterbalance the upheaval of what they are feeling;

- if a child suspects something is wrong but hasn't been told anything, it is easier for them to pretend nothing is wrong than to ask what is wrong;

- daydreaming enables them to carry on when feelings hurt too much;

- they can only handle short periods of intense feelings and then they need to get back to being normal to shield themselves from feeling awful;

- carrying on as normal distracts the child from feeling or asking scary questions;

- a child may not understand the relevance of what is happening or what they have been told;

- the news hasn't sunk in;

- nothing has been told to the child and because the child has no reason to think otherwise, there is no reason to think they would act any differently.

How to respond
Things to avoid

- Don't force a child to face what is happening or to cope in a certain way.

- Don't criticize or judge a child's way of coping — try to understand it.

- Don't express judgement toward them for carrying on with their normal life. This may contribute to guilt feelings in the child. An adult may need a long walk in the woods — a child may need to laugh and play ball.

Things to encourage

- Try to determine if the child has the proper understanding of the situation.

- Be open and honest to your child's level of understanding.

- Give small bits of information at a time.

- End discussions with your child telling you what has just been explained to them, and ask if there are any questions.

- Encourage your children to ask questions or talk about what they are feeling.

- Encourage your children to spend some time by themselves so they have the opportunity to think and feel without being watched.

- Accept the behaviour — this is the way the child is coping at this time.

- Over the course of a parent's illness, a child may have periods of pretending that nothing is wrong. These are usually to take a break from all the changes that are happening — to pretend that things are how they used to be.

When a child reacts with anger

A child may be angry because:

- sickness is causing disruptions in family life and normal routine and activities;

- they may feel abandoned (by the sick or healthy parent or both);

- they feel worried about the future;

- time and money problems limit activities and recreation;

- the parent got sick;

- the other parent is not the one who got sick.

How to respond

Things to avoid

Try not to scold a child for reacting to the illness with anger. Remember, this is a way of expressing feelings. Scolding may make them feel ashamed of their feelings. Be patient and in a quiet time after the angry behaviour passes, encourage the child to talk about their feelings.

Things to encourage

Let your child know that it is okay to show or let out anger, but that it has to be released in an acceptable way. In this way you are directly giving them permission to express and release it. Talk about how to manage it safely and without physically harming anyone or hurting other people's feelings, using examples such as screaming it out in the cellar, punching pillows or kicking milk cartons.

"Lots of kids your age feel ripped off and upset because of what has happened. We need to find a way for you to let those feelings out without bothering other people. That means you can't do things like yell at me or slam your door . . . What about. . . getting your hockey stick out . . . going to the park and hitting some balls . . . going down to the basement and screaming it out."

Try to assist the child to express anger through such statements as "you seem upset." Explore with them ways to express that they are angry.

Encourage lots of physical activity. Some children need to release bottled up feelings in a physical way. Active play can be a helpful outlet.

The child may feel ashamed about feeling angry. Let it be known that feeling angry is a normal reaction.

Let the child know it is normal to sometimes wish it was the other parent who was sick. Parents are loved differently at different times.

Prepare your children with responses to tell their friends.

When a child feels guilty

A child may feel guilt:

- for believing that feeling, saying or doing something made the parent sick;
- for wishing it was the other parent who was sick;
- for fighting with the sick parent in the past;
- for not being the "perfect child";
- for being angry that the illness is lasting so long;
- for feeling angry that his/her parent got sick;
- for being healthy and carrying on with normal living.

How to respond

- Clarify that it was nothing the child said, did or thought that made the parent sick. "Thinking thoughts cannot make bad things happen." "Mean thoughts did not make your mother sick."

- Reassure the child that the sick parent loves them, and that fighting or tension was forgiven a long time ago.

- Explain to the child that it is normal to sometimes wish it was the other parent who was sick, that they love each parent differently at different times.

- Mention that it is normal to feel impatient and to want life back to normal.

- Assure children that their feelings are commonly experienced by other children in the same situation. Discuss, for instance, difficult times of close friends (e.g. divorce, move from neighbourbood, death of a grandparent) and how that child felt then.

When a child seems afraid

A child may feel afraid because they are wondering:

- who will take care of me?
- will I be able to carry on with my normal activities?
- will I get cancer too?
- will my other parent get sick?
- is my mom going to die?
- did I cause the illness by thinking or doing something?
- why can't someone help my mom/dad?
- because the parent looks so different.

How to respond

- The child will usually feel less afraid if they are aware that many children worry about the same kinds of things.

- Children generally worry about today and tomorrow, not the future. Keep responses to fears in the same time frame.

- Children's feelings of security are usually maintained if you are honest with them.

- Reassure children that someone will always be there to take care of them.

- A very real fear for a child is that the other parent may get sick or die. Try not to address this lightly and don't make promises of which you are not absolutely sure. "I am healthy now and I expect to live for a long time." "I expect to live a long time, but if anything ever did happen to me, _____ would look after you."

- Reassure the child that it was nothing the child thought or did that caused the parent to become sick.

- Give information before it happens, if it is suspected that it will occur ("this might not happen but . . . "), so there is less surprise when it does.

- Try to give your child information before events/changes happen.

- If you suspect that something will happen, tell your children about the possibility so that it will be less of a surprise if it does happen.

- If your child cannot get past the belief that "cancer means death," and that the parent is going to die (maybe because of the child's previous experiences with cancer), you may find it helpful to give them some examples of people that your child knows of who have had cancer and who now are back to normal living (e.g. hockey player Mario Lemieux, skater Scotty Hamilton, singer Olivia Newton-John, and Tour de France cyclist Lance Armstrong). Of course, you can't give your child absolutes, but if the outlook for your disease is favourable, provide them with proof that many people overcome the disease.

Examples of other reactions a child may feel or show:

Helplessness
Confusion
Forgetfulness
Jealousy
Anxiety
Regression
Bodily distress (e.g. toileting accidents, headaches, stomach aches)
Take on some of the sick parent's role in the family.
Silence
Idealize the sick parent.
Sleep disturbances (e.g. nightmares)
Change in appetite
Frequent crying
Total focus on sick parent
Avoidance of reminders of the sick parent
Withdrawal into own little world a lot of the time
Sad
Constantly tired
Yearning and loneliness
Disbelief that anything is wrong
Blame his or herself for what has happened
Listlessness
Inability to concentrate on anything

Remember, if you are concerned with how your child is handling the situation, seek professional help.

6. Supporting your child

There are many ways of supporting your children. Some of the more important ones in this situation may be things such as: being honest and keeping children up to date, respecting how they are handling things, expressing your own feelings so that your children know it is normal and okay to show theirs, and, realizing that they need time and space to pretend that everything is normal. Supporting your children also means providing them with options so they don't feel pressured to do certain things.

Give your child choices

Most children, especially when they see that parents are stressed and upset, want to please — they want to do what is expected of them, they want to do what is right. They also want to act grown up and to feel included. This is all wrapped up in feeling confused and scared because of the unknown, and because of a lack of understanding of what is going on with their parent.

Try not to assume what children will want to do about being involved with their sick parent. You can support children a great deal by not giving them the added pressure of what you expect of them.

After you have given them the updated picture of what is happening and what they would see if they visited the hospital, provide children with options.

"Do you want to come to the hospital with me to see Mommy, or are you going to stay and play with _____ ?" Presenting it this way gives the child an out. You haven't presented it as an assumption that the child is going to come.

"You can come to the hospital and see Mommy, or you can talk to her on the phone, or you can draw her a picture and I will take it to her."

"Do you want to go to Nanny's for the weekend, or would you rather she come over here?"

Although children should not have the option of being updated on what is happening, they should have the option of how many times they hear the same explanation provided to others. "Grammy and Grampie are coming over this afternoon. I'm going to talk to them about what I told you this morning about Mommy. You can listen again if you want, or you can play."

Encourage expression of feelings, fears and concerns

Remind children frequently that they are not alone in the way they are feeling.

Ask your children to describe what they think is going on. You may gain some insight into their fears.

Explain that sometimes feelings are mixed up — that you can have many feelings about the same thing at the same time.

Explain that some feelings don't always make sense.

Share some of the feelings that you are having, but reassure your children that you are still in control and able to care for them. This will encourage them to express their own sadness. If parents don't express what they are feeling, the children will conclude it is wrong to express their pain and feelings.

Explain your feelings and behaviours before your child interprets them in his/her own way.

A child may find it easier to talk with another adult (other than his/her own parents) about what is happening. Parents should keep the person informed and share their ideas with this adult. Indicate approval of the relationship so the child doesn't feel guilty.

Encourage the child to let feelings out in a manner that is comfortable and familiar (e.g. talking, crying together, physical activity). If the child is feeling angry, talk about acceptable ways to let that out.

Helping a child give a name to what is being felt (e.g. angry, worried, scared) may give them control over those feelings. It is usually easier to work on feelings if you can identify or label what they are.

Children don't always express their feelings accurately because they don't know what the feeling is, or because they don't know the words. When children express feelings with statements such as, "I want Mommy to be home," or "I don't want Mommy to be in hospital," our natural reaction may be to say something like, "Oh, don't you want your mother to get better?" This can make children feel guilty. Really what they are probably trying to say is, "I miss Mommy." Try to respond to their feelings (e.g. "Is that because you are missing Mommy?") and let them know those feelings are normal and it is okay to feel that way.

Talk to your children about what feelings they may experience.

Help your children explain to their close friends what is happening.

Explain to children that they may experience new feelings about what is happening, or that their feelings may change and that is normal. Encourage them to let you know what they are feeling.

Crying

Reinforce that crying is normal and shows you are feeling sad.

Explain that crying may relieve some of the pain you have inside you.

Do cry in front of your children and explain to them why you are crying. It shows them that it is okay to cry in front of you.

Some children just cannot seem to get their tears started. Introducing a sad movie or story can sometimes cause emotions to be released and is a comfortable way for the child to express feelings.

Anger

If your child is angry and hostile, talk with him or her about how best to release some of the anger (e.g. physical activity, yelling it out behind closed doors). Explain that it is normal to feel this way, but that some ways of expressing it are better than others.

Encourage normal activity

Involve them in activities such as making cards for the sick parent or meal planning when Mommy is away.

Hugs and affection

Be sensitive, patient, and respond to moods and feelings. This can be very hard to do when you are stressed.

7. If you have concerns about your child

Children may have quiet times, they may have sad times, they may have angry times. Generally, the different feelings they experience come and go, and are mixed in with periods of normal living. This roller coaster of feelings is normal for children as they deal with a parent being sick and the changes it causes in their daily living.

When your child has continuing behaviour that does not appear to be helpful to the child, it may be time to seek help. When there are repeated changes in a child's performance at school, when there is ongoing change with friends and at play, when a child continues to withdraw from people, when they develop real eating problems or their sleep patterns are seriously affected, these may all be warning signs. Other disturbances that may be of concern are repeated changes in behaviour such as isolating themselves, being frightened much of the time, avoiding certain things, being very quiet (when they were not usually like that), or always worried that they are sick.

A parent may ask, "Should my child be seeing someone to help them through all of this?" If your child is aware of what is going on, if you are giving them the opportunity to ask questions, to discuss feelings, fears or concerns they may have, and they are not displaying repeated behaviours that you are concerned about, they probably have all the support they need at this time.

If you get the sense that your child is struggling and you think they may benefit from speaking to a counsellor, be careful how you approach the subject. You don't want your child to think that you think they're "crazy," nor do you want your child to think you don't want to deal with how they are feeling about things.

Make sure you check out the counsellor before your child sees him or her. You need to provide the counsellor with the current information on what is happening, how things have been explained to your child to date, what the situation looks like for the next while, and any concerns you have about your child. You also need to explore what the approach is going to be, if you agree with it, and if there is anything you can do.

A child that has become very quiet and remains quiet may be crying for help in their own way. Don't ignore it.

Where do you go for help?

Resource people who may be able to assist you in finding professional help for your child include: school counsellor; your family doctor; health care professional (e.g. social worker, psychologist, nurse) who is caring for the sick parent; someone from the Cancer Society or similar organizations; your minister or priest; or your community health nurse.

Qualified professionals who work with children dealing with all types of different losses can be found at the children's hospital nearest to you. At the hospital, there will be a program or service that you should be able to tap into. These programs have a variety of names such as Child and Adolescent Mental Health Services, Mental Health Services, Psychiatry Services, Department of Psychology. If you do not have a children's hospital nearby, contact the mental health services in the nearest hospital, or community mental health program. They should be able to help you find someone. Your family doctor or community health nurse can also link you up with these mental health services.

8. Selected books explaining and dealing with serious illness

Books for children

Toddlers (about 2½–5 years)

Berger, Melvin. (1985). *Germs Make Me Sick.* New York: Harper and Row.

Boulden, Jim, and Boulden, Joan. (1995). *When Sickness Happens.* California: Boulden Publishing. (Tel.: 1-800-238-8433). Describes the feelings a child may experience when someone close is seriously ill, how they may look, talk, act, and how they may need medicine and machines.

Boulden, Jim, and Boulden, Joan. (1995). *Someone Special is Very Sick.* California: Boulden Publishing. (Tel.: 1-800-238-8433). Describes the fears and feelings a child may experience when a family member is seriously ill. An elaboration of *When Sickness Happens,* with activity pages for the child to complete.

LeBlanc, Sophie. (1997). *A Dragon In Your Heart*. Beauport, Quebec: MNH Inc. Available in French *(Un Dragon dans le Coeur)* $10. (Fax: 1-888-666-8961 to order.) Written by a mother with breast cancer for her 5-year-old daughter. Good illustrations. Detailed explanation of cancer and how chemotherapy works.

Merrifield, Margaret. (1995). *Morning Light*. Toronto: Stoddard Publishing. Gently explains the serious illness of a single mom who has AIDS. Mother dies at the end of the story with the son and daughter having to learn to adjust to life as things carry on. (Excellent)

Parkinson, Carolyn Sterns. (1991). *My Mommy Has Cancer*. Rochester, New York: Park Press. This book for young children (ages 3-6) explains cancer and chemotherapy using bubbles to explain cancer cells and how chemotherapy works.

Vigna, Judith. (1993). *When Eric's Mom Fought Cancer*. Illinois: Albert Whitman and Co. Eric's mom has breast cancer and the story describes some of the events and feelings the family experiences.

Young school age (about 5–8 years)

American Cancer Society. (1987). *It Helps to Have Friends When Mom or Dad Has Cancer.* (Booklet). Tel.: (404) 320-3333.

Berger, Melvin. (1985). *Germs Make Me Sick.* New York: Harper and Row.

Boulden, Jim, and Boulden, Joan. (1995). *When Sickness Happens.* California: Boulden Publishing. (Tel.: 1-800-238-8433). Describes the feelings a child may experience when someone close is seriously ill. Describes how a person may look, talk and act, and how they may need medicine and machines.

Boulden, Jim, and Boulden, Joan. (1995). *Someone Special Is Very Sick.* California: Boulden Publishing. (Tel.: 1-800-238-8433). Describes the fears and feelings a child may experience when a family member is seriously ill. An elaboration of *When Sickness Happens,* with activity pages for the child to complete.

Boulden, Jim, and Boulden, Joan. (1995). *When Someone Is Very Sick.* California: Boulden Publishing. (ph: 1-800-238-8433). Different issues are addressed that can arise when a family member has prolonged illness: the taking of medicines; fatigue; deteriorating physical appearance. The book demonstrates and validates feelings of sadness, fear, worry, loneliness and love. Contains activity pages for the child to complete. An older child's version of *Someone Special Is Very Sick.*

Goodman, Michelle. (1990). *Vanishing Cookies: Doing O.K. when a parent has cancer.* Geared to 7-12 years.

Harpham, Wendy Schlessel. (1997). *When A Parent Has Cancer.* New York: HarperCollins. See Books for Parents (page 92) for description of adult portion of book which contains a glossary

85

for children. Included with the hardcover book is a separate book, *Penny and the Worry Cup*, which fits into a slot in the back of the main book. This little paperback that fits in a slot in the back of the main book is written for children about the third grade level and tells the story of a 7-year-old's experience and how she copes with her mother's cancer. It is written for about a third grade level child and tells the story of a 7-year-old's experience and how she copes with her mother's cancer. *Penny* can be read by child or parent.

LeBlanc, Sophie. (1997). A *Dragon In Your Heart*. Beauport, Quebec: MNH Inc. Available in French *(Un Dragon dans le Coeur)* $10. (Fax: 1-888-666-8961 to order) Written by a mother with breast cancer to her 5-year-old daughter. Good illustrations. Detailed explanation of cancer and how chemotherapy works.

Merrifield, Margaret. (1995). *Morning Light*. Toronto: Stoddard Publishing. Gently explains serious illness of a single mom who has AIDS. Discusses the ups and downs of everyday living. Mother dies at the end of the story with the son and daughter having to learn to adjust to life as things carry on. Contains additional information for parents. The reader could certainly interchange the word "cancer" for "AIDS" when reading the story.

National Cancer Institute. (1995). *When Someone In Your Family Has Cancer*. Fax (301) 402-5873.

Parkinson, Carolyn Sterns. (1991). *My Mommy Has Cancer*. Rochester, New York: Park Press. This book for young children (ages 3-6) explains cancer and chemotherapy using bubbles to explain cancer cells and how chemotherapy works.

Vigna, Judith. (1993). *When Eric's Mom Fought Cancer.* Illinois: Albert Whitman and Co. Eric's mom has breast cancer and the story describes some of the events and feelings the family experiences.

Older school age (about 8–12 years)

American Cancer Society. (1987). *It Helps To Have Friends When Mom Or Dad Has Cancer.* Tel. (404) 320-3333.

Boulden, Jim, and Boulden, Joan. (1995). *When Sickness Happens.* California: Boulden Publishing. (Tel.: 1-800-238-8433). Describes the feelings a child may experience when someone close is seriously ill. Describes how a person may look, talk and act, and how they may need medicine and machines.

Boulden, Jim, and Boulden, Joan. (1995). *When Someone Is Very Sick.* California: Boulden Publishing. (Tel.: 1-800-238-8433). Different issues are addressed that can arise when a family member has a prolonged illness: the taking of medicines; fatigue; deteriorating physical appearance. The book demonstrates and validates feelings of sadness, fear, worry, loneliness and love. Contains activity pages for the child to complete. An older child's version of *Someone Special Is Very Sick.*

Canadian Cancer Society. (1995). *When Someone You Love Has Cancer.*

Clifford, Christine. (1998). *Our Family Has Cancer Too!.* Minnesota: Pfeifer-Hamilton Publishers. Some of the events and feelings a family experiences through a mother's diagnosis and treatment of breast cancer is described by the sixth grade son. The author (the mother in the story) creates a positive, healthy and family oriented approach that gets the points across in an easygoing style with humour and cartoons. This may be a "cool" way to get information across to children who haven't been keen to listen or talk.

Goodman, Michelle. (1990). *Vanishing Cookies: Doing O.K when a parent has cancer.* Geared to 7-12 years.

Harpham, Wendy Schlessel. (1997). *When A Parent Has Cancer.* New York: HarperCollins Publishers. See Books for Parents (page 92) for description of adult portion of book. Included with the hardcover book is a separate book, *Penny and the Worry Cup.* This little paperback that fits in a slot in the back of the main book is written for children about the third grade level and tells the story of a 7-year-old's experience and how she copes with her mother's cancer. Penny can be read by child or parent.

LeShan, Eda. (1986). *When A Parent Is Very Sick.* Toronto: Little, Brown & Company. Explores many feelings and reactions children and teens experience as a parent goes through an illness, from diagnosis to death. Provides a range of feelings that they may experience. My only caution to this useful resource is in chapter two. The author explains that feelings and thoughts (past and present) have a lot to do with a person getting sick and that feelings influence the immune system. If you don't agree with this, don't have the child read this section, or discuss after the child has read it.

LeShan, Eda. (1972). *What Makes Me Feel This Way? Growing Up With Human Emotions.* New York: Aladdin Books. MacMillan Publishing. This is a book about feelings. It explores a variety of feelings that a child/adolescent may experience as they grow up and helps the reader try to understand them. Particularly useful if a child does not want to talk about feelings.

Merrifield, Margaret. (1995). *Morning Light.* Toronto: Stoddard Publishing. Gently explains serious illness of a single mom who has AIDS. Discusses the ups and downs of everyday living. Mother dies at the end of the story with the son and daughter having to learn to adjust to life as things carry on. Contains additional information for parents. The reader could certainly interchange the word "cancer" for "AIDS" when reading the story. (Excellent)

National Cancer Institute. (1995). *When Someone In Your Family Has Cancer.* Fax (301) 402-5873.

Strauss, Linda. (1985). *Coping When A Parent Has Cancer.* New York: Rosen Publishing Group. Walks pre-teens and adolescents through many of the events and feelings they will experience. Easy reading, good explanations, detailed (a lot of reading).

Adolescents

American Cancer Society (1987). *It Helps To Have Friends When Mom Or Dad Has Cancer.* (Booklet). Tel.: (404) 320-3333.

Canadian Cancer Society. (1995). *When Someone You Love Has Cancer.*

Clifford, Christine. (1998). *Our Family Has Cancer.* Minnesota: Pfeifer-Hamilton Publishers. The events and feelings a family experiences through a mother's diagnosis and treatment of breast cancer is described by the sixth grade son. The author (the mother in the story) creates a positive, healthy and family oriented approach which gets the points across in an easygoing style with humour and cartoons. This may be a "cool" way to get information across to children who haven't been keen to listen or talk.

Harpham, Wendy Schlessel. (1997). *When A Parent Has Cancer.* New York: HarperCollins. See Books for Parents (page 92) for description of adult portion of book which contains a glossary for children. Included with the hardcover book is a separate book, *Penny and the Worry Cup.* This little paperback that fits in a slot in the back of the main book is written for children about the third grade level and tells the story of a 7-year-old's experience and how she copes with her mother's cancer. *Penny* can be read by child or parent. May be a bit young for this age group, but can still provide a sense of what is normal and teens can read it by themselves.

LeShan, Eda. (1986). *When A Parent Is Very Sick.* Toronto: Little, Brown & Co. Explores many feelings and reactions children and teens experience as a parent goes through an illness, from diagnosis to death. Provides a range of feelings that they may experience. My only caution to this useful resource is in chapter two. The author explains that feelings and thoughts (past and present) have a lot to do with a person getting sick and that feelings influence the immune system. If you don't agree with this, don't have the child read this section, or discuss after the child has read it.

LeShan, Eda. (1972). *What Makes Me Feel This Way? Growing Up With Human Emotions.* New York: Aladdin Books. MacMillan Publishing. This is a book about feelings. It explores a variety of feelings that a child/adolescent may experience as they grow up and helps the reader try to understand them. Particularly useful if a child does not want to talk about feelings.

National Cancer Institute (1995). *When Someone In Your Family Has Cancer.* Fax (301) 402-5873.

Strauss, Linda. (1985). *Coping When A Parent Has Cancer.* New York: Rosen Publishing Group. Walks pre-teens and adolescents through many of the events and feelings they will experience. Easy reading, good explanations, detailed (a lot of reading).

Books for parents

American Cancer Society. (1993). *After Diagnosis: A Guide For Patients and Families.*

Canadian Cancer Society. (1997). *Talking With Your Child About Cancer.*

Fine, Judylaine. (1984). *Afraid to Ask: A book for families to share about cancer.* Toronto: Window.

Fitzgerald, Helen. (1992). *The Grieving Child.* Toronto: Fireside. Chapters on preparing for possible death, how children react to death, dealing with your child's emotional response, and adjusting to a new life, give specific direction to helping a parent deal with the emotional responses and behaviours, and when you should be concerned about these responses and behaviours. This book deals with a variety of losses, illness and death being two of the losses explored.

Harpham, Wendy Schlessel. (1997). *When A Parent Has Cancer.* New York: HarperCollins. One of the few in-depth books on the subject of raising children when a parent has cancer. The author proposes approaches for preventing and responding to common problems in a healthy way. Contains glossary for children. If you are concerned with how a child is reacting and you are wondering what to do or if they need professional help, this is one of the few books that will provide you with some direction. Also included is a separate book, *Penny and the Worry Cup*. This little paperback that fits in a slot in the back of the main book is written for children about the third grade level and tells the story of a 7-year-old's experience and how she copes with her mother's cancer. *Penny* can be read by child or parent.

Jarratt, Claudia Jewett. (1994). *Helping Children Cope with Separation and Loss*. Boston: Harvard Common Press. This in-depth book examines separation and loss due to a variety of changes: sickness, divorce, death, etc. Parents, other caregivers, teachers, health care providers, any adult involved with a child may find this book helpful. The author discusses telling children about loss, helping them face change, understanding and supporting grief, facilitating the grief process, helping children with sadness, anger and aggression, and responding to problems of self-esteem. Excellent resource but detailed and a lot of reading.

McCue, Kathleen. (1994). *How to Help Children Through A Parent's Serious Illness*. New York: St. Martin's Press. Chapters include: how to explain illness to children of different age groups, warning signs (disturbances in behaviour that may indicate a child is in trouble), how to help with emotions, preparing children for hospital visits, having a sick parent at home, the future, dying and death. This is one of the few in-depth books on this subject. It gives parents excellent direction on how to explain illness but most of the book describes how to provide guidance through the entire experience. If you are concerned with how a child is reacting and you are wondering what to do or if professional help is needed, this is one of the few books that will provide you with some direction.

Munroe, Judy. (1990). *The Facts about Leukemia*. Toronto: Chestwood House. Explains leukemia, who gets it, and all about the disease in children's terms.

Other resources

Videos

Kids Tell Kids What It's Like When Their Mother or Father has Cancer. This video contains descriptions from children, who have a sick parent, talking about what it feels like to have a parent with cancer and what helps them feel better. Cancervive. 1998. To obtain the video: www.cancervive.org or call 310-203-9232.

My Mom Has Breast Cancer. This video presents childrens' responses to the diagnosis of their mothers' breast cancer. The children and mothers interviewed describe their reactions and feelings and how they learned to cope during this experience. To obtain the video: www.kidscope.org or call 404-233-0001.

Talking About Your Cancer: A Parents Guide To Helping Children Cope. Fox Chase Cancer Centre. 1996. To obtain the video: 215-728-2668

Why Charlie Brown, Why? American Cancer Society. Charlie Brown's friend gets leukemia. Treatment takes place over the seasons, giving the child a sense of how long chemotherapy can take. Cartoon.

Web sites:

www.cancer.ca — Canadian Cancer Society. Information under publications
www.cancer.org — American Cancer Society
www.cancernet.nci.nih.gov — National Cancer Institute
www.oncolink.upenn.edu — University of Pennsylvania Cancer Centre
www.cancercare.org — Cancer Care
www.cancervive.org — Cancervive
www.kidscope.org — Kidscope

9. When a parent is dying

Often the reaction to a parent dying is to think, "I will go home and tell the kids after their mother has died, after I leave the hospital." Most parents feel terrified and totally unprepared for telling their children that their mother or father is dying, or has just died.

Children appear to adjust better to the death of a parent if they know the parent is going to die before it happens. As they get older they readjust more smoothly when they have said their goodbyes, when they have felt included and have felt part of the whole experience. Although it may not seem totally necessary to have young children be part of things as a parent is dying, it will be important to these children when they are older. Whether they were too young to remember, or have forgotten over time, they will want to know if they were part of this family event. "Did I say goodbye to Mommy?" "Did I visit her in the hospital?"

Even if children have to be told over the phone because of the distance, they should know about the death before it happens. As much as the healthy parent or guardian wants to tell them in person, it is more important for the children to know what is happening before the death occurs. Prepare the adult looking after the children beforehand for what you are going to tell the children. Borrow phones from neighbours for each child if there are other jacks in the house, and have the adult listen in on one of the extensions. After the parent has died, the children should be among the first to know — by phone or by the person caring for them.

Many children do not understand the effect the death will have on their lives or they are too young to really understand what is going on. Spending some time with family in the parent's room, in the waiting room, or in a family member's house can help them feel a part of things. Although adults want to protect children from seeing adults who are sad and crying, seeing these reactions can help them realize that others are feeling sad, mixed-up and lonely. You probably don't want to have them with adults who are very expressive with their feelings (moaning, wailing, sobbing) unless they are used to seeing these reactions.

When a child visits or wants to stay in the waiting room with other family, make sure you bring toys and books along. They can play alongside everyone and tune the conversation in and out. If they know that they are going to be kept up to date, they often tune out what is around them, feeling comfortable that someone will fill them in if things change. Remember that children generally can't focus on intense topics for very long. They need periods of time when they can escape into their play world.

Usually parents feel a great sense of relief after they have told their children the parent is dying. Many feel that once it has been explained and children have said their goodbyes, a huge pressure is lifted and they are able to focus on being with their loved one.

Build on what the children already know and walk them through what is going to happen.

"Remember that we told you that Mommy has a kind of cancer that isn't going to get better, and that she is getting sicker. Well the doctors told us today that Mommy is now very sick. Mommy isn't going to come home again. Mommy is going to die. Nobody knows when that will be — it may be today, it may be tonight, it may be tomorrow or in a couple of days. I will tell you when she dies."

After children are told their parent is going to die, they need to be given the opportunity to say their goodbyes. Try not to put pressure on children by asking them a yes/no question. Instead, give them options. Before you give them options, explain what they will see.

"Mommy is in bed and she is sleeping a lot. Her eyes are shut most of the time. She still has that tube in her arm. She has the railing around her bed so she won't fall out and hurt herself. Grammy is sitting beside her holding Mommy's hand. Grammy is very quiet because she is so sad."

"I am going to go back in with Mommy and sit with her. If you want, you can come and say goodbye. If you want to give her a kiss, I can lift you up onto the bed. Or I can say goodbye to Mommy for you and you can stay here and play with your toys. Aunt Sue can stay here with you, and I will come in and see you once in a while. Or you can go back home with Aunt Sue."

In your conversation, you may want to remind them that this may be the last time they see Mommy.

Children should never be forced to do anything they don't want to do. They should be given choices after they learn what they will see.

Small children need to be included in the goodbyes (as with everything else). They will probably copy what their older sisters and brothers do. In their own way, they will feel a part of things. In the future, when they are dealing with this, it will help them to know they were included.

Because unexpected events can happen, try to give children a sense of what could possibly happen.

"As you know, Mommy is not going to get any better. Mommy is not going to live for very long but we aren't exactly sure when she is going to die. I will certainly tell you if we know when Mommy is close to dying, but there is always a chance that something could happen and Mommy could die when we don't expect it. Every time you say goodbye to Mommy now, it could be the last time you see her. I just wanted to tell you this in case that happens."

If you are concerned that your children may mention this to their mother and it may cause too much sorrow, tell them not to talk about it with her because it makes her too sad.

If the parent is unconscious, give the children guidance. "Mommy isn't waking up now, but we are still talking to her and holding her hand and kissing her."

Examples of explaining probable death

- Mommy is not getting better — she is getting sicker.

- Mommy has a sickness that the doctors can't fix.

- Mommy is so sick that she is going to die.

- You know your mom has been sick for a long time and the doctors have tried to help her. Well, today they told us that she isn't going to get better.

- Your mom isn't going to get better. She is going to die, and probably will very soon.

- The doctors would like to be able to fix Mommy but they can't.

- I will tell you if things change.

- Mom is getting worse. She will probably die in a few days.

- Your mother is not going to get better. It looks like she will die tonight. Do you want to be there tonight or do you want to go in now and say goodbye?

- Don't start planning how you are going to react when your mom dies. There is no right or wrong way. What you feel will just come naturally.

- I'm feeling scared right now. How are you feeling?

- I don't think she will ever get well again.

- You will be able to spend whatever time you want with your mother even though she is very ill.

When the parent is unconscious

- No one knows how much your mom can hear or feel right now. Talk to your mom like you usually would. Although she can't answer back, she may be able to hear what you are saying and it will make her feel happy to know you are here.

- Say the things you would like to tell your mom, because she may hear you.

- Touching your mother is also a good way of connecting. You can hold her hand.

10. When a parent dies

Children need to be told promptly that a parent has died. It is important that they hear it from someone close to them before they hear it by accident from someone else. They need to be told what will happen over the following few days. They need ongoing reassurance that the surviving parent or others close to them are going to stay nearby.

The understanding and meaning of dying and death varies, depending on the developmental stage of the child. Each child needs to have an explanation in order to understand that the parent is no longer present, and why those around may be behaving differently.

For most children under 2½ or 3, they cannot understand the concept of death. Include them in your conversations with older children but do not expect them to grasp too much. They will take their clues from others. They will pick up that something is wrong. They may feel distressed and insecure, but what has happened is beyond their understanding. They need love and security and routine.

Children usually need to understand the practical issues around death. You may find it easier to separate this subject from your religious ideas about afterlife. The practical issues usually include questions like: "What happens to the body before and after it goes in the coffin?", "What happens in the ground?", "What is cremation?", "What is left after the body is burned?", "What do you do with the ashes?"

The remaining parent needs to explain death using ideas from his or her own religious/belief system. For many adults, trying to explain a belief system and answer children's questions is the first time in a long time that they have really thought about what they believe. If you do not have definite ideas about after-life, share this with your children. It may provide them with comfort to know that these ideas are not clear, solid and well understood by all. Let them know that different people have different ideas, and that as they get older, they will add to or change their ideas. Young children do not deal with abstract concepts very easily unless the ideas are familiar to them. Regardless of what children understand, they need to: feel included in what is happening; be comfortable expressing concerns and fears; not feel abandoned; and feel cared for and loved.

Throughout the days following the death, the child needs to be with someone they like, trust, and who is comfortable with the situation. The person should remain close or be available to the child to give support, affection, guidance, and to answer questions.

Saying goodbye and funerals

Children need to have the opportunity to say goodbye to their deceased parent.

For many children, just like adults, there are different kinds of goodbyes. Many children need a private, quiet goodbye with just immediate family present. Some families go into the church or funeral home before a funeral and have a private goodbye. Others say it by writing a poem or drawing a picture. For still others, it may be simply saying goodbye in their prayers. Some children need to have private partings as well as participate in the rituals of wakes, funeral home visitation and funeral. Offer suggestions as to how your children can say their last farewells.

Explain what is going to happen over the next few days, why it happens, and what exactly it will look like (e.g. what is a funeral, who will be there, what will people be doing, how long it will be, can someone leave if they do not want to be there). After you explain things to your children, decide together what they are going to do. Maybe attending the funeral reception instead of the funeral is a good compromise for younger children.

"I am going to go to the funeral home to see people who knew Mommy. You can bring some books and come. Aunt Sue will be there to stay right beside you. Or you can stay here with Aunt Sue until I come home."

"If you come to the funeral, Aunt Sue will stay with you all the time. You can bring some books to read. If you decide you don't want to stay, you and Aunt Sue can leave and we will see you after the funeral is over."

Funerals take place to make things real, to say goodbye, to give support, and to express grief. If children are going to attend the funeral, ensure a calm adult, well-known to the children accompanies each child. Children should know they always have the option of leaving the funeral once there.

Tell your children if extra family will be staying at the house or if there will be a lot of visitors. Many older children and teenagers find the extra turmoil and attention very overwhelming. Respect their privacy. If they want to be at a friend's home, show them your acceptance and give them some space.

Some children ask to see their deceased parent. You know your child best. Talk it over with them, explaining what their parent now looks like. If you feel that it is the right thing to do, that it will help the child more than it will upset them, give them the option. "We can go in and see Mommy, or we can remember Mommy as she was when she was alive."

Grieving

As with illness, children react to the loss of a parent using a wide range of feelings and behaviours. They may go through many of the feelings and behaviours they have already experienced throughout the parent's illness, only more intensely. Each will have their own way of grieving, of reacting. For children who have been aware of the impending death, they may have already started working through some of their feelings and fears, but it doesn't necessarily mean the grieving will be any easier.

As with serious illness, children shouldn't be protected from emotional pain and sadness. There is no way of keeping a child from hurting. If it doesn't happen at the death, it will happen later on. It is better to let the child feel included and begin to grieve with those who are experiencing the same loss. If they do it later, they may feel isolated, lonely, and wonder if their feelings are normal.

In their own way, children will participate in the loss and grieving of their parent.

Children may need to pretend for periods of time that everything is the way it used to be. They will probably experience many of the same feelings they had throughout the illness: anger, guilt, sadness, fear (of other parent getting sick, dying).

Hidden grief never goes away. If you have concerns about a child, get help.

If after a few weeks your child: isn't sleeping; isn't eating; won't go to school; is doing very poorly in school; is continually acting out; leaves the room when anybody mentions the dead parent's name; is lashing out at everybody; can't talk about anything that has happened; doesn't want to play with any friends; or if you just sense that she or he is in trouble, get help. Talk to your family doctor, a health professional, a school counsellor, a minister or a priest. They will try to help find someone who can assess your child.

Examples of explaining death

- When someone dies, they don't come alive again.

- She can't feel anything. Her body doesn't work anymore. She doesn't breathe or see or feel.

- The body dies. We keep the memory of the person alive.

- People don't need their bodies any more, so we bury them.

- Death is the end of life.

- Most people live until they are very very old. You probably will. Every once in a while people die when they aren't so old, like your mother.

- When someone is dead, they don't breathe. The body stops working. Everything stops.

- When someone is dead, the person does not breathe. The body is still and peaceful.

- Dead is not like on the cartoon where something dies and comes back again.

- We will never see her again, but we can remember her, talk about her and look at pictures of her.

- You know, I wonder about what happens when people die too. No one knows for sure, but I believe _____ .

- Would you like to hear some of my thoughts?

- It will take a long time before you feel settled inside yourself.

- You didn't do anything to make your mother die. Nothing you said, did or thought had anything to do with your mother dying.

11. How children understand and cope with death

Toddlers (about 2½–5 years)
Understanding of death

- believe death is reversible, temporary; person is in another place, living; person will come back (because they do on TV); does not understand that death is final; death is like sleep — parent will wake up again;

- believe they control death;

- have very limited understanding. Aware that something upsetting has happened, but not sure what it is;

- because of lack of understanding of death, the child does not necessarily view it as bad or sad;

- don't see death as happening to self;

- don't understand abstract words like God, heaven, hell, angel, soul;

- understand that dead things don't move;

- may begin to wonder how death happens, what will happen to body, will I die?

How a parent can help

- Do not describe death as "going to sleep." A child is then frightened to go to sleep.

- Keep to concrete, simple and straightforward explanations. Children at this age don't usually understand abstract ideas.

- Unless a child has a familiarity and comfort with religious explanations (e.g. heaven, spirit, soul, angel, afterlife), be careful how you use them in your explanation. It may make what is happening even scarier. Connect death to words they have some familiarity with — for example "God," "church." When they are older and familiar with the words, ideas can be shared.

- A child isn't familiar with descriptions such as "expired," "moved on," "gone to their maker," or "passed away." Use "died" or "dead."

- Don't use the explanation that a parent died because he or she was so good, or because God needed her more than we did, or that a parent has gone to a "better" place.

- Painting too beautiful a picture of what happens when a person dies may make the child want to join the parent.

- Try not to link suffering and death to sin, punishment or reward.

- Reinforce that they did not cause the death.

- Maintain as normal a routine as possible.

- Try and be patient as children become clingy. Being close makes them feel secure.

Young school age (about 5—8 years)

Understanding of death

- sees dying as a physical thing only;

- believes that death is "done" by someone or something bad (i.e., boogeyman, angel, ghost), not a bodily process, believe that they cause death;

- still generally confused about religious ideas that are used in describing death and dying;

- may understand that death is final, irreversible;

- usually associates death with a tragic event;

- wants the details surrounding dying and death (e.g. how do you eat or go to the bathroom in the coffin?);

- afraid and confused about the idea of death;

- may understand the concept of a soul/spirit.

Death reactions

- may pretend that the parent is still alive for periods of time;

- prepare the child for periods of sadness, and for experiencing feelings not felt before;

- may become very clingy to remaining parent;

- worry about deceased in coffin;

- worry that remaining parent may leave them.

Older school age (about 8–12 years)

Understanding of death

- dying is not just a physical thing, but both physical and spiritual

- death is the termination of life, end of physical life, end of bodily function

- death is brought about naturally as well as by accident

- able to understand that soul functions apart from body (if in family belief system)

Death reactions

- may feel isolated for being different from friends

- fear of personal safety

How a parent can help

- Because the child is now able to understand abstract thinking to a certain degree, you can begin to share personal philosophical and religious beliefs of illness and death, including uncertainties and unknowns, to help them develop their own ideas.

- It can often take months before a child wants to discuss what has happened. Keep communication lines open and indicate that you are certainly thinking about things.

Adolescents

Understanding of death

- if family's tradition is such that they believe in an afterlife, the adolescent is usually able to discuss death as a process involving something more than the end of life;

- seeking philosophical and religious answers or explanations.

Death reactions

- can feel guilty for past conflict with deceased parent;

- angry that parent died;

- worried about own health;

- may look for the meaning or value of parent being sick;

- questions the meaning of life and death;

- questions their own life and values and the impact of their own being.

How a parent can help

- Be prepared to spend time with your teen as they try to make sense of what has happened.

- Be prepared to share some of your ideas with them.

- Be honest with your ideas. Because your teen is able to understand abstract thinking, you can begin to share personal philosophical and religious beliefs of illness and death, including uncertainties and unknowns, to help them develop their own ideas.

- Let them know that any disagreements they had with their parent were long forgotten and that their parent loved them very much.

- Tell them it is normal for them to sometimes wish it was the other parent who had died.

- Share your feelings of being angry and feeling ripped off. It will help them understand that what they are feeling is normal.

- Do not make them feel guilty for going out with their friends. "Mom would want you to continue on with your life."

12. Selected books explaining and dealing with death

Books for children

Toddlers (about 2½–5 years)

Althea series. (1982). *When Uncle Bob Died*. Great Britain: Dinosaur.

Breebart, J. and Breebart, P. (1993). *When I Die, Will I Get Better?* New York: Peter Bedrick Books. A sick rabbit dies and friends experience different feelings after he dies.

dePaola, Tomie. (1978). *Nanna Upstairs and Nanna Downstairs*. New York: Puffin Books.

Greenlee, Sharon. (1992). *When Someone Dies*. Atlanta: Peachtree. Explains very simply what happens when someone dies and some of the feelings/fears the child may experience.

Heegaard, Marge. (1988). *When Someone Very Special Dies*. Minneapolis: Woodland Press. Explains death in a very simple concrete way. Has a good introduction of reminders for parents.

Hogg, Elaine Ingalls. (2000). *Remembering Honey*. Halifax, Nova Scotia, Canada: Nimbus Publishing. Twins experience their pet dying and cope with it differently (anger, sadness). After their dog dies, they begin to remember the funny and nice times they shared.

Brown, Laurie Krasny, and Brown, Marc (1996). *When Dinosaurs Die. A Guide To Understanding Death*. New York: Little, Brown and Co. Explains what alive and dead means in very simple terms. Also explores the feelings around death, how you say goodbye, the different customs around death, and what comes after death. A really good book to introduce these different topics.

Limb, S. (1993). *Come Back Grandma*. New York: Alfred A. Knopf.

Mellonie, Bryan, and Ingpen, Robert. (1983). *Lifetimes. A Beautiful Way To Explain Death To Children*. Toronto: Bantam Books.

Merrifield, Margaret. (1995). *Morning Light*. Toronto: Stoddard Publishing. Describes the illness and death of a mother with AIDS.

Palmer, Pat. (1983) *"I wish I could hold your hand ..." A child's guide to grief and loss*. California: Impact.

Prestine, Joan Singleton (1993). *Someone Special Died*. Torrance: Frank Schaffer Publications Inc. This book is from the "Kids Have Feelings, Too" series. It very simply explains a young girl's feelings for someone special who has died (and a bit about death). See Books for Parents page 126 for corresponding Parent Resource Guide.

Shriver, Maria. (1999). *What's Heaven?* New York: St. Martin's Press. A mother describes her ideas of heaven to her child with the child putting things into her own words and adding her own ideas. The mother also describes her ideas of what a soul is and answers questions about being buried.

Vigna, Judith. (1991). *Saying Goodbye to Daddy.* Toronto: General Publishing Limited; and Illinois: Albert Whitman and Co. A father dies suddenly in a car accident. Good explanations of dying and death suitable for any type of death. Describes the disruptions and feelings a young child may experience.

Viorst, Judith. (1971). *The Tenth Good Thing About Barney.* Hartford: Antheneum Publishers. A boy's cat dies, which stimulates discussion about heaven, burial, and how the cat's body contributes to new life after it is buried.

Wilhelm, Hans. (1985). *I'll Always Love You.* New York: Crown Publishers. A young boy's dog gets old and dies. The boy finds comfort in the fact that he has always told his dog how much he loves him.

Young school age (about 5–8 years)

Althea series. (1982). *When Uncle Bob Died*. Great Britain: Dinosaur.

Breebart, J. and Breebart P. (1993). *When I Die, Will I Get Better?* New York: Peter Bedrick Books. A sick rabbit dies and friends experience different feelings after he dies.

Boulden, Jim. and Boulden, Joan. (1995). *When Death Happens*. California: Boulden Publishing. (Tel.: 1-800-238-8433). Describes what death is and how you may feel when someone dies.

Boulden, Jim. and Boulden Joan. (1994). *Goodbye Forever*. California: Boulden Publishing. (ph: 1-800-238-8433). This book will help a child understand the concept of death as a natural process; how death is different from sleep, saying goodbye, burial and understanding and accepting different feelings.

Boulden, Jim, and Boulden, Joan. (1992). *Saying Goodbye*. California: Boulden Publishing. (ph: 1-800-238-8433). An older child's version of *Goodbye Forever*.

Carrick, Carol (1976). *The Accident*. New York: Ticknor & Fields: A Houghton Mifflin Company. This book explains the feelings (e.g. anger, sadness, loneliness) a young child has when his dog is hit by a car. The story is about the boy's grief and how he has to say his goodbyes so that he can move on.

Greenlee, Sharon. (1992). *When Someone Dies* Atlanta: Peachtree. Explains very simply what happens when someone dies and some of the feelings and fears that go with loss.

Hogg, Elaine Ingalls. (2000). *Remembering Honey.* Halifax, Nova Scotia, Canada: Nimbus Publishing. Twins experience their pet dying and cope with it differently (anger, sadness). After their dog dies, they begin to remember the funny and nice times they shared.

Brown, Laurie Krasny. and Brown, Marc. (1996). *When Dinosaurs Die. A Guide to Understanding Death* New York: Little, Brown and Company. Explains what alive and dead means in very simple terms. Also explores the feelings around death, how you say goodbye, the different customs around death, and what comes after death. A really good book to introduce the different topics.

LeShan, Eda. (1978). *Learning To Say Goodbye: When A Parent Dies.* New York: Avon. Explores the feelings, events and behaviours that children, teens and parents have surrounding death, the funeral, grieving and starting a new life.

LeShan, Eda. (1972). *What Makes Me Feel This Way? Growing Up With Human Emotions.* New York: Aladdin Books. MacMillan Publishing. This is a book about feelings. It explores a variety of feelings that a child/adolescent may experience as they grow up and helps the reader try and understand them. Particularly useful if a child does not want to talk about feelings.

McFarlene, Sheryl, and Lightburn, Ron. (1991). *Waiting for the Whales.* Victoria, BC: Orca Books. This book for young children describes a young girl's close relationship with her grandfather and how she remembers him when he dies.

Merrifield, Margaret. (1995). *Morning Light.* Toronto: Stoddard Publishing. Gently explains the serious illness of a single mom who has AIDS. Discusses the ups and downs of everyday living. Mother dies at the end of the story with the son and daughter having to learn to adjust to life as things carry on. Contains additional information for parents. The reader could certainly interchange the word "cancer" for "AIDS" when reading the story. (Excellent).

Palmer, Pat. (1983) *"I wish I could hold your hand ..." A child's guide to grief and loss.* California: Impact.

Prestine, Joan Singleton. (1993). *Someone Special Died.* Torrance: Frank Schaffer Publications Inc. This book is from the "Kids Have Feelings, Too" series. It very simply explains a young girl's feelings for someone special who has died (and a bit about death). See Books for Parents page 126 for corresponding Parent Resource Guide.

Sanford, D. (1986). *It Must Hurt A Lot: A Child's Book About Death* New York: Multnomah. Describes several different feelings people experience with death. Uses comparisons from other aspects of life.

Simon, Norma. (1986). *The Saddest Time.* Illinois: Albert Whitman and Co. One of the three stories is about a young uncle who dies after a long illness and the feelings the nephew experiences in the days after.

Shriver, Maria. (1999). *What's Heaven?* New York: St. Martin's Press. A mother describes her ideas of heaven to her child with the child putting things into her own words and adding her own ideas. The mother also describes her ideas of what a soul is and answers questions about being buried.

Temes, Roberta. (1992). *The Empty Place. A Child's Guide Through Grief.* New Jersey: Small Horizons.

Vigna, Judith. (1991). *Saying Goodbye to Daddy*. Toronto: General Publishing Ltd; and, Illinois: Albert Whitman and Co. A father dies suddenly in a car accident. The author provides good explanations of dying and death suitable for any type of death. This book also describes the disruptions and feelings a young child may experience.

Viorst, Judith. (1971). *The Tenth Good Thing About Barney*. Hartford: Antheneum Publishers. A boy's cat dies, which stimulates discussion about heaven, burial, and how the cat's body contributes to new life after it is buried.

Wilhelm, Hans. (1985). *I'll Always Love You*. New York: Crown Publishers. A young boy's dog gets old and then dies. The boy finds comfort in the fact that he has always told his dog how much he loves him.

Older school age (about 8–12 years)

Boulden, Jim, and Boulden, Joan. (1995). *When Death Happens* California: Boulden Publishing. (Tel. 1-800-238-8433). Describes what death is and how you may feel when someone dies.

Boulden, Jim, and Boulden, Joan. (1992). *Saying Goodbye.* California: Boulden Publishing. (Tel. 1-800-238-8433). An older child's version of *Goodbye Forever.*

Boulden, Jim, and Boulden, Joan. (1994). *The Last Goodbye I.* California: Boulden Publishing. (Tel. 1-800-238-8433). Activity book with exercises dealing with the feelings and issues that surround death. Includes discussion around sadness, anger, fear, guilt, acceptance, responsibility, depression, funerals, and what happens after death.

Carrick, Carol. (1976). *The Accident.* New York: Ticknor & Fields: A Houghton Mifflin Company. This book explains the feelings (e.g. anger, sadness, loneliness) a young child has when his dog is hit by a car. The story is about the boy's grief and how he has to say his goodbyes so that he can move on with life.

Grollman, Earl. (1993). *Straight Talk About Death For Teenagers. How To Cope With Losing Someone You Love.* Boston: Beacon Press.

Krementz, Jill. (1991). *How It Feels When A Parent Dies.* New York: Alfred A. Knopf.

LeShan, Eda. (1978). *Learning To Say Goodbye: When A Parent Dies.* New York: Avon. Explores the feelings, events and behaviours that children, teens and parents have surrounding death, the funeral, grieving and starting a new life.

LeShan, Eda. (1972). *What Makes Me Feel This Way? Growing Up With Human Emotions.* New York: Aladdin Books. MacMillan Publishing. This is a book about feelings. It explores a variety of feelings that a child/adolescent may experience as they grow up and helps the reader try to understand them. Particularly useful if a child does not want to talk about feelings.

Merrifield, Margaret. (1995). *Morning Light.* Toronto: Stoddard Publishing. Gently explains the serious illness of a single mom who has AIDS. Discusses the ups and downs of everyday living. Mother dies at the end of the story with the son and daughter having to learn to adjust to life as things carry on. Contains additional information for parents. The reader could certainly interchange the word "cancer" for "AIDS" when reading the story. (Excellent)

Palmer, Pat. (1983) *"I wish I could hold your hand ..."* A child's guide to grief and loss. California: Impact.

Powell, E. Sandy. (1990). *Geranium Morning.* Minnesota: Carolrhoda Books. A book for preteens describing feelings and behaviours of grief after the death of a parent.

Sanford, D. (1986). *It Must Hurt A Lot: A Child's Book About Death.* New York: Multnomah. Discusses several different feelings people experience with death. Uses comparisons from other aspects of life.

Simon, Norma. (1986). *The Saddest Time.* Illinois: Albert Whitman and Co. One of the three stories is about a young uncle who dies after a long illness and the feelings the nephew experiences in the days after.

Smith, Doris Buchanan. (1988). *A Taste of Blackberries.* New York: HarperTrophy. Describes the feelings a pre-adolescent boy experiences after the sudden death of his best friend.

Shriver, Maria. (1999). *What's Heaven?* New York: St. Martin's Press. A mother describes her ideas of heaven to her child with the child putting things into her own words and adding her own ideas. The mother also describes her ideas of what a soul is and answers questions about being buried.

Temes, Roberta. (1992). *The Empty Place. A child's guide through grief.* New Jersey: Small Horizons

Vigna, Judith. (1991). *Saying Goodbye to Daddy.* Toronto: General Publishing Limited; and, Illinois: Albert Whitman and Co. A father dies suddenly in a car accident. The author provides good explanations of dying and death that are suitable for any type of death. This book also describes the disruptions and feelings a young child may experience.

Adolescents

Boulden, Jim, and Boulden, Joan. (1994). *The Last Goodbye II* California: Boulden Publishing. (ph:1-800-238-8433). Adolescent version of *The Last Goodbye I*. Also includes discussion of suicide, forgiveness, and dealing with anger. Reader is encouraged to undertake activities.

Beckelman, Laurie. (1995). *Grief.* New Jersey: Crestwood House.

Grollman, Earl. (1993). *Straight Talk About Death for Teenagers. How to Cope with Losing Someone You Love.* Boston: Beacon Press.

Krementz, Jill. (1991). *How It Feels When A Parent Dies.* New York: Alfred A. Knopf.

LeShan, Eda. (1978). *Learning To Say Goodbye: When A Parent Dies.* New York: Avon. Explores the feelings, events and behaviours that children, teens and parents have surrounding death, the funeral, grieving and starting a new life.

LeShan, Eda. (1972). *What Makes Me Feel This Way? Growing Up with Human Emotions* New York: Aladdin Books. MacMillan Publishing. This is a book about feelings. It explores a variety of feelings that a child/adolescent may experience as they grow up and helps the reader try to understand them. Particularly useful if a child does not want to talk about feelings.

Books for parents

Fitzgerald, Helen. (1992). *The Grieving Child.* Toronto: Fireside. Chapters on preparing for possible death, how children react to death, dealing with your child's emotional response, and adjusting to a new life, give specific direction to help a parent deal with the emotional responses and behaviours, and when you should be concerned about these responses and behaviours. This book deals with a variety of losses, illness and death being two of the losses explored.

Gaffney, Donna. (1988). *The Seasons of Grief. Helping Children Grow Through Loss.* New York: Plume. Practical. Asks and gives many examples of answers to many of the typical questions children have.

Grollman, Earl. (1990). *Talking About Death: A Dialogue Between Parent & Child.* Beacon Press: Boston: Beacon Press. Easy to read, covers a lot of important information for children of all ages.

Grollman, Earl. (editor) (1967). *Explaining Death To Children.* Boston: Beacon Press.

Harpham, Wendy Schlessel. (1997). *When A Parent Has Cancer.* New York: HarperCollins Although this book is geared to when the parent has the illness, it will also be very useful in understanding children's reactions and giving you recommendations on how to respond. One of the few in-depth books on the subject of raising children when a parent has cancer. The author proposes approaches for preventing and responding to common problems in a healthy way. Contains glossary for children. If you are concerned with how a child is reacting and you are wondering what to do or if they need professional help, this is one of the few books that will provide you with some direction. Also included is a separate book, *Penny and the Worry Cup* which fits into a slot in the back of the main book. It is written for children about the third grade level and tells the story of a 7-year-old's experience and how she copes with her mother's cancer. *Penny* can be read by child or parent.

Huntley, Theresa. (1991). *Helping Children Grieve When Someone Dies*. Minneapolis: Augsburg.

Jackson, Edgar. (1965). *Telling A Child About Death*. New York: Hawthorn/Dutton.

Jarratt, Claudia Jewett. (1994). *Helping Children Cope with Separation and Loss*. Boston: Harvard Common Press. This in-depth book examines separation and loss due to a variety of changes: sickness, divorce, death, etc. Parents, other caregivers, teachers, health care providers, any adult involved with a child may find this book helpful. The author discusses telling children about loss, helping them face change, understanding and supporting grief, facilitating the grief process, helping children with sadness, anger and aggression, and responding to problems of self-esteem. Detailed and a lot of reading.

Kroen, William C. (1996). *Helping Children Cope With the Loss of a Loved One*. Minneapolis: Free Spirit Publishing Inc. This is a very practical and easy-reading guide for adults. The author explains how children understand death and provides the reader with guidelines for helping children understand. He explains how children grieve and offers guidelines for helping children work through grief. He also offers suggestions on how to remember a loved one, and help children move on with life. Provides the adult with support.

McCue, Kathleen. (1994). *How To Help Children Through A Parent's Serious Illness*. New York: St. Martin's Press. Although this book is geared to when the parent has the illness, it will also be very useful in understanding children's reactions and giving you recommendations on how to respond. Chapters include: how to explain illness to children of different age groups, warning signs (disturbances in behaviour that may indicate a child is in trouble), how to help with emotions, preparing children for hospital visits, having a sick parent at home, the future, dying and death. This is one of the few in-depth books on this subject. It gives parents excellent direction on how to explain illness but most of the book describes how to provide guidance through the entire experience. If you are concerned with how a child is reacting and you are wondering what to do or if professional help is needed, this is one of the few books that will provide you with some direction.

Prestine, Joan Singleton. (1993). *Helping Children Cope With Death*. Torrance: Frank Schaffer Publications Inc. A Practical Resource Guide for *Someone Special Died*. This resource is intended to help adults help young children through the feelings most children experience after the death of someone they love. See corresponding book for children in Books for Children, page 114.

Schaefer, Dan, and Lyons, Christine. (1986). *How Do We Tell The Children? Helping Children Understand and Cope When Someone Dies*. New York: Newmarket Press.

Schneiderman, Gerald. (1989). "When A Parent Dies" in *Coping With Death in the Family*. Toronto: NC Press Ltd.

Temes, Roberta. (1984). *Living with an Empty Chair: A Guide Through Grief.* New York: Irvington Publishers. A chapter on children gives parents some direction.

Vigna, Judith. (1991). *Saying Goodbye to Daddy.* Toronto: General Publishing Ltd.; and, Illinois: Albert Whitman and Co. A father dies suddenly in a car accident. The author provides good explanations of dying and death suitable for any type of death. This book also describes the disruptions and feelings a young child may experience

Web sites:

www.cancer.ca — Canadian Cancer Society. Information under publications

www.cancer.org — American Cancer Society

www.cancernet.nci.nih.gov — National Cancer Institute

www.oncolink.upenn.edu — University of Pennsylvania Cancer Centre

Key points to consider

As soon as you can, be open and honest with your children.

Cover the dying issue right from the start. Probably the hardest thing for everyone will then be in the open and no one will have to be on their guard.

Involve your children in what is happening so they feel included.

Keep children informed about plans for them, their sick parent and their healthy parent over the next while.

Avoid surprises whenever possible. Tell your children you will keep them up to date with what is going on with their parent. "If anything changes, we will let you know." If you tell them this, be sure and keep your promise.